The Sage
of Petaluma

by J. Abner Peddiwell

THE SABER-TOOTH CURRICULUM

The Sage of Petaluma

AUTOBIOGRAPHY OF A TEACHER

by J. Abner Peddiwell

WITH A FOREWORD

BY HAROLD R. W. BENJAMIN

McGRAW-HILL BOOK COMPANY

New York   Toronto   London

*This book is dedicated
with respectful admiration
to readers of*
THE SABER-TOOTH CURRICULUM
*who saw in those paleolithic lectures more
than the author thought he had put into them*

Foreword

AS I read this mythical autobiography of the Sage of Petaluma, I am worried lest some careless reader think the story may be true, and I am haunted by a feeling that it is true.

These events never happened to anybody in particular, yet they happened to everybody of my generation and background. J. Abner Peddiwell never rode in the Punitive Expedition of 1916, never saw the Bois de Belleau on that delicate June morning, and never crawled onto the bleak beach of Massacre Bay.

But some of us did, and we may be held by the imaginary forces he causes us to assemble there.

Peddiwell never trod the Ochoco trails or taught the Danebod homesteaders' children. He never attended the University of the West or held professorial rank in Dead Coon Lake College by-the-Woods. He never sang the songs and told the stories, worked and fought, or loved and hated as he claims to have done.

But some of us did, and we may wish to examine his tale. We need to judge how much he had to lie in order to tell the truth about himself and his times.

With the exception of certain well-known historical figures, as, for example, Rain-in-the-Face and John J. Pershing, all the characters in this book are fictitious. None of them is intended to resemble any real person, living or dead.

Peddiwell is of course most completely a myth, yet he has been real in his effect on me. I am grateful to him for the most of it. He introduced me to thousands of school men and women whom I might not otherwise have known. He helped give me students ready to use their imaginations as well as their memories. No professional colleague can do more than that.

The old professor did get me into occasional difficulties by leading students, fellow teachers, prospective employers, and even two or three of my nearest kinswomen to believe me a connoisseur of tequila or other distilled liquors. This undeserved reputation has perhaps left a faint scar on my personality.

The influence of Peddiwell later caused the proprietor of the longest bar in the world to offer me free samples of tequila daisies or other related drinks, to the extent of my personal capacity, whenever I might come back to his frontier city. It also led various travelers of my acquaintance to bring me a total of gallons of the fiery Mexican spirit as libations to paleolithic learning.

It is perhaps useless, in view of the reputation thus innocently acquired, to add that I never returned to Tijuana, and that I gave all donations of tequila to hospitals, laboratories, and a few individual investigators.

One item remains definitely on the wrong side of the ledger in my accounts with J. Abner Peddiwell. In spite of the *Ph.D.* that he never omits from his formal signature, he has made some of my most scholarly colleagues suspect me of academic heterodoxy. This suspicion is baseless. I believe in timeless culture as much as anybody, almost—excepting extremists, of course, like . . .

But let Peddiwell name names.

Harold R. W. Benjamin

Contents

Author's Preface

"THOSE WHO have actually lived through historical events, as I have," Theodor Mommsen once observed sardonically, "know very well that history is neither written nor made without love and hate."

The autobiographer is peculiarly susceptible to the handicap implied in this dictum. In his double role of actor in and interpreter of a particular set of historical events, he must bear in mind his loves and hates. He must look at them as dispassionately as possible. He must not minimize them, he must not exaggerate them, but he cannot ignore them. If he tries to do so, he will be led into atrocious assaults upon the truth. He must let his readers know what his loves and hates are, so far as he is able to identify and describe them. The readers can then make the necessary allowances to get an approximation of the truth. They can do this job better than he can.

I like most autobiographies. I like to make the love-and-hate adjustments on the scale of truth in each case.

The autobiographer may say in effect, "I acted nobly in this instance because I was brave;" while from my smug position of readership I say, "You acted that way automatically and because you were afraid to differ from your class, and now that you are under the opiate of your own rhetoric you dope out these verbalisms concerning nobility and courage."

Or the author may say, "I did the wrong thing at this point. I did not mean to be evil. I was just reacting to my evil environment. I was following the example of evil companions." Whereupon with renewed sneers I interpose, "You got into difficulty because you like to alibi. All your life you have kept explaining why you could not do this and why you had to do that. There was nothing basically wrong with you that a few good doses of leather would not have cured in the first ten years of your existence."

Autobiographers have two main faults; they tell too much or they tell too little, often simultaneously. Whether they claim to tell all or say that they are dealing only with the more significant of their experiences, they commonly start to lie as soon as they put pen to paper. Few of them deliberately falsify the account. They merely try to give a true picture according to their loves and hates.

I am rough on these autobiographers. It is fair, therefore, to invite the readers of this story to scrutinize it with the same kind of severity. I will give them the data as well as I can. Let them discover my loves and hates for use in making necessary adjustments on the scale of truth.

Only great men or especially lucky ones should be allowed to write autobiographies. If I belong here at all, it is in the latter category. In this book, therefore, I shall attempt to document the fortune which seemed to me to justify its writing. This is an account of parts of my educational life and times. It seeks to describe my learning, not only in formal educational institutions but also in other places where I have had my ways changed by instruction.

Who can say that the professor lecturing to me and fifty-nine other sleepy sophomores on why Tertullian was never elevated to sainthood was schooling me on a higher level than was the workman in the stone quarry who showed me how to hit the head of a steel drill with an eight-pound hammer, alternating my strokes with his in steady rhythm of sixty blows per minute? Was an appreciation of *When in disgrace with fortune and men's eyes* ever educationally more necessary to me than the soldier's rule of no excuse? What is the minimum level of knowledge required for a proper education at any stage of learning?

I know thousands of men and women who can answer such questions. There are millions, without doubt, who think they can answer inquiries of this kind correctly. I am not among them. I am hampered by convictions. One of these convictions is that such topics as history of the Church fathers, striking drill, appreciation of poetry, acquisition of military attitudes, and levels of knowledge are blind alleys for the investigation of educational comprehensiveness, tone, or quality.

Here is a primary datum of love and hate for the reader's immediate use.

If my story seems to deal with war to a marked degree, it is because war has been a powerful schoolmaster to me and the men of my generation. I will not comment on the quality of the curriculum, but the quantity has certainly been considerable. If J. J. Webster and Medicine Horse loom in these pages as educators comparable in caliber to William Preston MacFarland and Poplar Branch Handelman, it is precisely because those four men were my greatest teachers, in the order of rank here listed.

Permit me to remark finally to readers of my own generation that this story is as much about you as about me. I grew up with you. I rode and worked with you. I fought by your sides, and too often I saw you die young. Now I regard you with deep interest. I have to observe you from the spot where I happen to be standing. I can see you only through my own eyes. I have to try to figure you out in terms of my own experiencces.

J. Abner Peddiwell, Ph.D.
Petaluma State University

*The Sage
of Petaluma*

ONE

Heritage
of My Fathers

I AM J. ABNER PEDDIWELL simply because I
have no first name, only a first initial. Furthermore, I do not have
the initial legally. I took it without benefit of custom or clergy
and added it to my signature, not to hide anything of which I was
ashamed but to display something of which I was proud. How I
happened to do this is a story that goes back to James Jonathan
Webster of Juniper Wells, Montana, and the Oregon Ochoco
Valley.

When I say Mr. Webster's name even now, it seems to me
that everyone within hearing should brighten in instant recognition. Of course I know that very few persons living today, other
than a handful of aged men and women in isolated communities
of Northeastern Montana and Central Oregon, have ever heard of
J. J. Webster, yet my surprise at a blank look on the face of one
to whom I speak the name is still automatic and, for a moment at
least, tinged with pity and perhaps a trace of contempt.

This reaction is obviously unreasoned. It is tied to long vacation days when I was home from the academy, days when I would
ride until I came to a ranch house where I was not known at once
under the disguise of added inches and years since last I had been
seen. Even the *Bar-W* or *J-J* on my horse's near hip might not
give the immediate cue. There would be polite invitations to the

young stranger to dismount and have dinner. This courtesy was warm in those days and that country, but it was nothing to the reception touched off when someone found out who I was.

I always anticipated with delight the supreme moment of discovery, trying to act like an ordinary, drifting wrangler, some poor homesteader's son, all the while waiting for that first exuberant yell. It made little difference, so nearly as I can now recall, whether the announcement of my identity came from a hand's recognition of my mount, a woman's decision that she had taught me in Sunday school, or my own statement.

When I made the announcement myself, I tried to sound modest, but I suspect that I never completely succeeded.

"I am Mr. Webster's adopted son, Abner Peddiwell."

Then the explosion came. Chairs tipped against the wall hit the porch floor with a bang. Men in the process of unsaddling slipped leather from cinch ring and vaulted corral rails. Women erupted from the house with outstretched hands.

"Why dog my cats if you ain't Mr. Webster's oldest!"

"Put 'er there, Ab! My stars, how you've growed!"

"Honey, I'm gonna kiss you! I'm yore cousin!"

The effect was always the same, instant, electric. It showed in every man's voice, in every woman's eyes. All the world seemed to be saying, "It is a great thing to be Mr. Webster's son."

That was what I thought too.

I was always conscious, however, that I was not Mr. Webster's real son the way my little brother, Jim, was. I never claimed or allowed anyone else to assume otherwise. I pointed out the foster relationship.

No one else ever did. Jim introduced me as, "My big brother, Ab." The women who signaled kissing kinship were related by blood only to Mr. Webster and not at all to me, but they never betrayed notice of the fact. All the community knew that my name was *Peddiwell* and not *Webster,* knew indeed that I came from a stock alien to their Yankee clans, but they treated me as though the knowledge meant nothing to them.

They all took their lead on this matter from James Jonathan

Webster himself. He never gave a sign that he wanted to pass me as a blood kinsman, but at the same time he treated me precisely as he treated Jim, with due allowance for differences in age and personality. He never suggested, for example, that I take the name of *Webster,* and at no point in my boyhood or since did I ever consider the change. Yet I cannot remember when I did not know and accept as entirely natural the fact that Mr. Webster's will left his estate to Jim and me in equal shares, with an annuity to Jim's mother if she were found, and provided that if I had reached my majority I was to be named executor and Jim's legal guardian during his minority. This was because I was Mr. Webster's older son. Anyone surprised by the terms of the will would have had to be someone who did not know Mr. Webster.

I never called him anything but *Mr. Webster,* and he never called me anything but *Abner.* He was not given to the use of nicknames, diminutives, endearing epithets, or titles. You could tell what Curly's or Shorty's real names were when you heard the boss speak to them.

This idiosyncrasy was related to Mr. Webster's adherence to the frontier maxim that one man is as good as another and sometimes a damned sight better. That was why he never said *Kid* or *Bub* to a young man. The boy was intrinsically the equal of Captain Hathaway or Judge Purdom, whom Mr. Webster called *Charles* and *William* respectively.

These are the facts on this matter with my added speculation, but I do not pretend to know what they meant in terms of Mr. Webster. He remained a mystery to me in many important ways from the hour of my first memory of riding in his arms through the spring snowstorm to that final day when I eased his body from the saddle.

I started out to tell how I came to put the *J.* in front of my name, but now I see I have to go back a little further and tell how I came to be Mr. Webster's foster son.

My real father was a drifting ranch hand who said his name was *Abner Peddiwell.* He had probably originated somewhere near the Kentucky-Tennessee border. He was remembered by Mr.

Webster and others who knew him in the West as having referred on occasion to both those states as "home." My father once told Levi Kingman, the Bar-W foreman, that he desired not to attend the Decoration Day exercises being conducted at Coyote Point by the Grand Army of the Republic. Since both the foreman and the owner were members of that organization of Union veterans, Levi was startled by the boy's refusal. The younger punchers commonly regarded this or any other day of patriotic observance as an opportunity for convivial recreation while the old soldiers were suffering oratory and saluting colors.

Apparently young Peddiwell sensed the foreman's surprise, for he added politely that he took this decision to keep the hell away from all that sort of Yankee foofarrow in particular view of the fact that his own father had served under the command of the great Rebel general, Nathan Bedford Forrest. This item is a strong indication that my paternal grandfather was a resident of Kentucky, Tennessee, Mississippi, or possibly Alabama. Forrest generally recruited his soldiers from those states.

I have little doubt that much of Levi Kingman's early liking for my father was derived from the boy's military kinship to Bedford Forrest. The foreman had vast respect for the general's memory, mingled with a half-ashamed affection which he tried to mask with profanity. He had served as a trooper in an Indiana cavalry regiment and had fought in George Waring's brigade on June 10, 1864, when that gallant officer had tried to hold Brice's Crossroads against Forrest's vanguard while Brigadier General Samuel D. Sturgis was bringing his infantry forward.

Levi Kingman, a precise and colorful raconteur, often told the story. "There we was," he would begin matter-of-factly, "with fourteen hundred men to start that there fight. We had Colt's repeatin' carbines, and they was good weapons for them days. What's more, we had six fine field guns. And what did them Rebs have? Well, sir, they had nine hundred cav'lrymen, armed with sawed-off, muzzle-loadin' Enfields, and not a single God- damn' cannon, but they whipped hell out of us. Then Colonel Winslow come up with a couple thousand more troopers for our side and ten more cannon, and the Rebs got up twelve hundred more cav'lrymen but still no field guns, and they went right ahead and whipped us some more. Finally it was past noon, and Old Sturgis got up our infantry at last. They was five thousand of 'em, and they had eight more guns. I don't know what the bald-faced hell they had been doin'. They only had five miles to go when that fight begun, but it took 'em three hours to get there. The Rebs about this time brought up eight guns and some more cav'lrymen, so then we started the real battle. On their side was four thousand Rebs, all cav'lry, and eight cannon. On our side was five thousand infantrymen, three thousand four hundred cav'lrymen, and twenty-four guns. And they still whipped hell out of us. When night come, them in our Army that wasn't dead, wounded, or captured was sure lightin' a shuck fer Memphis."

Here Levi would pause, as though to invite questions from the audience. Then he would raise the crucial inquiry himself. "How the hell could they do it? Their men was not a damn' bit better'n ours, nor their officers neither—the ones I knowed. Their small arms was nowhere near's good as ours. We outgunned 'em in cannon three to one. We outnumbered 'em two to one. How did they do it? Well, I'll tell you. They had one thing we didn't have, one thing we sure couldn't match. They had that black-whiskered bastard of a Forrest. He was the best that the God-damn' Rebel Army had *anywhere,* and he was sure one great, big hell of a lot better than any of them commanders Old Cumpsie Sherman ever throwed against him."

I was a college student before I made the mistake of remarking to Levi that the histories of the Civil War that I had read never seemed to say much about Nathan Bedford Forrest. The old man snorted, "Yeah, I guess that's right. The God-damn' Northerners don't wanta talk about him. It still gives *them* the jim-jams even to think about him. And the God-damn' Rebels, all they can think about is their two-bit West-Pointers. It was lucky for our side that Jeff Davis and Brax Bragg was half-witted enough to keep blockin' Forrest, trippin' him up, and takin' his men and his guns away from him. If they'd of had sense enough

to give him room accordin' to his size and strength, if they'd of
just let him have the troops he raised hisself in them four-five
states, if they'd of let him keep the guns and ammunition and
blankets and rations and wagons and horses and mules he stole
from us, he'd of took Detroit, and then what *I* wanta know is
where the hell would Sherman of been on his march to Atlanty,
and fur as that goes where would old Abe of been in the '64
election?"

I have never found the name *Peddiwell* on any Confederate
muster roll or discovered a person bearing that name in Kentucky, Tennessee, or anywhere else. It is possible that my father
adopted it for private reasons as he came North and West. It is not
very probable, however. An unschooled farm boy would hardly
have imagined such a name *de novo*. If he had really removed to
Montana one jump ahead of the sheriff, as some of his detractors
later suggested, he would likely have selected a more common
alias to confuse the trail. I think *Peddiwell* was his real name.

The known facts about my father are simple and scanty. He
rode up to Juniper Wells, Montana, and then out to the Bar-W in
the spring of 1890 with a horse and saddle he had borrowed from
a ranch forty miles to the south. He had previously been walking
long distances. The charitable ranch owner had fed him, furnished the transportation which he was to return at his convenience, and sent him to Mr. Webster for possible employment.

The Bar-W owner liked the looks of this errant teenager. No
doubt the shy, hungry-looking boy aroused the older man's ready
compassion for the underdog. In any event he was hired.

Thus began the association between the two men which was
to be ended only by death. It was a relationship marked by mutual esteem, even affection, and, since the younger man was eighteen years of age and the older was forty-four, by something of a
father-son feeling.

Young Peddiwell worked on the Bar-W for two years, first as
a horse wrangler and then, as his roping skill increased, as a regular cowhand. In the spring of 1892, he married Hilda Swanson
(or Swenson), a waitress in the restaurant at Coyote Point, who

had emigrated from Sweden a few months earlier. He had previously taken up a claim and built a cabin near the head of Juniper Creek in the foothills of the Hunkpapa Range. He took his bride there. With the help and under the protection of the Bar-W, he started running a few cows but continued to work on the big ranch at haying and round-up times. He was regarded by everyone, including himself, as a permanent Bar-W man.

My father was said to have had a reputation for industry and peacefulness. Although he wore a six-gun by custom of the time and was as good a shot as the average cowhand, he was never known to get into so much as a fist fight. I have been told that this was because he was not a drinking man. He was not in the habit, even on a most festive occasion, of taking more than a single shot of whiskey, although Levi Kingman testified that Abner Peddiwell knew how to make mighty good drinking liquor out of corn and sugar and sometimes did so. This stuff, said Levi, was a hell of a lot better and safer than anything sold in the saloons at Coyote Point.

The testimony on this matter swings the evidence toward Kentucky as my father's home state.

I was born in the cabin on Juniper Creek, March 30, 1893, at the cost of my mother's life. On March 15, 1895, my father died under circumstances hereinafter to be related. When he had been buried in ground still frozen so hard that blasting powder had to be used to dig the grave, Mr. Webster wrapped me in two soft, Oregon City blankets made into a papoose-carrier with safety pins from my personal baggage and shawl straps from his saddle, as he showed me many years later, and carried me the sixteen miles to Juniper Wells.

I cannot remember my mother, having, as I suppose, never seen her. I have tried hard to remember my father. I was almost two years old when he died, and it seems that I should have retained some memories of him, however vague and indistinct. I regret that I have been unable to revive even one. I can remember nothing about him, the cabin on Juniper Creek, or the Hunkpapa woman who cared for me. Except for one other object, the only

mementoes I have of my father are his .44-40 Frontier Colt, his
Model 73 Winchester of the same caliber, and a little shovel he
was whittling for me out of a broken axe handle at the time of his
death. The toy was designed to be presented to me on my second
birthday. Since my father had it almost finished, the two weeks
remaining before my birthday would have given him ample time
to put the last touches on it in the evenings after I was asleep.
Mr. Webster carried it in his carbine scabbard when he brought
me to Juniper Wells. He gave it to me punctiliously on the morning of March 30.

I have no direct memory of this event, but I never tired of
hearing Mr. Webster describe it. He spoke of it in our last conversation. My regiment was aboard the train, and the conductor
was checking his watch before giving the highball, when Mr.
Webster suddenly remarked, "I said, 'Here's a birthday present,
Abner, that your father made for you,' and you took it with a
laugh, said, 'Thank you,' in good English, and hugged that little
shovel close to you."

The old gentleman, then in his seventy-second year, turned
to stare at the locomotive. The conductor raised his lantern.

Mr. Webster turned to me, grasped my hand, and shook it
warmly. "I loved that boy, Abner," he said, "and I didn't rightly
know it till after he was dead."

I was so astonished I did something I had never done before.
I embraced Mr. Webster warmly just as the conductor shouted,
"All aboard," and the train started to move.

The next time I signed the payroll, I wrote my name, *J. Abner Peddiwell*. The battery clerk, with the alertness of his pen-
pushing tribe, cried, "Hey! That ain't the way we got it typed.
Your name is just *Abner Peddiwell*, according to the records."

"Change the records then," I said. "That's my name from
now on."

And it has been.

TWO

North-South Axis

THOSE STUDENTS of child development who suggest that practically all memory begins with the acquisition of language would perhaps say that I learned my first words on that ride through the snow after my father's funeral. I think I have memories of that occasion, memories that appear to be independent of later information. No one except Mr. Webster and me ever knew, for example, that I sat on the bucking roll part of the way. He did not mention this fact to me in my early childhood, as nearly as he and I could recall when I was an undergraduate. I remember in clear detail that I sat sidewise on the near shoulder of the roll, facing the saddle horn. I can feel again the sting of the snow as it hit my forehead. I can sense the powerful movements of the horse as he struggled through the drifts. Most unforgettable of all, I can hear Mr. Webster's voice, cool yet with warm overtones, crisp but deliberate, vigorous but modulated. His famous kinsman, the Yankee statesman, could have had no better speaking instrument. Perhaps it was an inflection, an intonation, or even a word from that voice that constituted my first lasting memory.

There is some evidence contrary to this theory. Mr. Webster testified in later years that when he first brought me to Juniper Wells I had little English and spoke the Hunkpapa dialect of the

Prairie Sioux (more properly the Lacotah) language with remarkable fluency for a two-year-old. As I have previously mentioned, the woman who cared for me from my birth to my father's death was a Hunkpapa. My father was said to have known something of that language. Mr. Webster himself spoke Lacotah readily but with the accent and vocabulary of the Minneconju.

Since I began to learn or relearn Lacotah at the age of six, it is possible that in later years Mr. Webster's memory of my early linguistic attainments was not entirely accurate.

I have tried by introspective methods to determine which was my first language. I have repeated words with which I was presumably familiar at the age of two, and I have attempted in each case to judge the tongue that seems to fit the concept more naturally. The results are inconclusive. The English word *shovel,* for instance, has a warm meaning for me. I seldom hear it without a quick thought of a small piece of carefully carved hickory. I do not know the Lacotah word for it or indeed whether such a word exists in that language. On the other hand, *sunka wakan* to me still means *horse* much more completely than does the English word. When I think of some truly distinguished horse, moreover, like *No Name, Man of War,* or my own *Toot Sweet,* the Lacotah term often comes first to my mind. Many English words associated with religion, like *church, prayer, holy,* and *God,* will always remain a little foreign to me beside their sonorous Lacotah counterparts. All these associations, of course, may have been made when I came into contact with Indians again upon my entering school at the age of six.

By the time I was five, I was certainly speaking English fluently in my roles of elder brother to three-year-old Jim and supporting actor in the dramas that were always being produced in the vicinity of Clarissa Webster, Jim's mother.

I was Mr. Webster's but not Clarissa's son. Until I started to write this page, I had never really examined this fact before. Certainly I had never regarded it as unusual. Now that I have to explain it, however, I can see that it was a circumstance that could have happened only with Mr. Webster and Clarissa. (I must go back a long way to show how it did happen.)

Mr. Webster was born in 1846 near Bennington, Vermont. In 1855 his father died of pneumonia, or lung fever, as it was then called, whereupon his mother sold their little farm and followed her two brothers to the Territory of Minnesota. For three years she resided in St. Paul, supporting herself and her four children by labors as a seamstress and straw-hat maker. Her oldest child, James Jonathan, helped her substantially by working in a livery stable. He was rated first as a boy roustabout, but before he was twelve he was promoted to fullfledged hostler.

The younger children assisted their mother by braiding straw for the hats, each small laborer having his daily stint rigorously imposed and faithfully executed. Mr. Webster remarked of this period, "My little brother and sisters didn't have much time to play. They always had those stints to finish. I used to try to help them when I got off work at the livery stable, but I kept going to sleep. Seems like that braiding kind of hypnotized me."

Since Mr. Webster's own stint in the livery stable probably averaged fourteen hours a day, the chances are that he needed no hypnotic inducement to sleep.

In the panic of 1857, Mr. Webster unfortunately lost his job with its steady income of $1.25 per week. A grown man, kinsman of the livery stable proprietor, had to have it to support his family. Mr. Webster's mother could still make straw hats but it was hard to sell them. Money for food was very scarce. There was no work for many adults and none for children. James Jonathan was almost twelve, Frederick Morse was ten, Eleanor was seven, and Harriet was four.

During the winter of 1857–58 the family lived almost exclusively on corn supplied by one of Mrs. Webster's brothers. The grain had to be shelled by hand and then ground in a small coffee mill. It was cooked over a corncob fire supplemented with an occasional windfall of chips salvaged from the streets by James Jonathan and his little brother, Frederick Morse. These processes were not very difficult, however, as Mr. Webster once explained to Jim and me.

It was at breakfast one morning when we were still small boys. We had been chided by the cook for not having eaten all the oatmeal in our bowls. Mr. Webster seemed to be telling his story in defense of a child's right to dislike a particular food. "The hard part," he explained, "was to eat that mush morning, noon, and night, without a drop of milk or sweetening in it. I have eaten corn since, of course, when I was in the Army or out on the trail where there was nothing else to do but eat it or starve, but if I don't have to I'll never touch a kernel of it again. It's not that I've got any prejudice against it. It's just that I've never seemed to relish it since the winter of '57."

Jim and I stared at our oatmeal, with its cream and sugar embellishments, and began to eat it thoughtfully.

In the spring of 1858 Mrs. Webster, assisted by her brothers, took up a claim in Southern Minnesota and started to farm it with the help of her children. They all worked. The first year was hard, the second and third were easier, and by 1861 the family was entering upon a period of relative prosperity.

Although some fifteen-year-old boys answered Lincoln's first call for volunteers, and the recruiting officers accepted anyone's word on his age if he looked big enough to carry a rifle, Mr. Webster had no intention of entering the Army. Everybody was sure the war would be ended long before he reached the age of eighteen. He knew how much he was needed at home, now that prices were going up and crops were good. He stayed on the homestead, breaking new land with the family's yoke of oxen, and putting in grain. As labor shortages began to be felt with the departure of the regiments, he began to work for wages on other farms wherever opportunity offered. With more money, he planned to buy additional cattle and perhaps a team of horses.

In 1862 when Little Crow and his Santee Sioux warriors struck the white settlers, Mr. Webster was working for a neighbor fifteen miles away. His mother and brother were among the recognizable dead. His sisters may have been taken captive, but they were not among those recovered when Little Crow's band was rounded up.

Thereupon, at the age of sixteen, Mr. Webster joined an infantry regiment, first fighting the Sioux in Minnesota and then being shipped East in April, 1863. His first engagement against the Confederates was at Gettysburg where his regiment lost three commanding officers in forty-five minutes. On the third day of fighting in the Wilderness in 1864, he was wounded severely in the breast. He spent the winter of 1864–65 in a Washington hospital, rejoining his regiment shortly before Appomattox. He was discharged in the grade of sergeant at the age of nineteen.

Mr. Webster never went back to live on the Minnesota farm. "I couldn't seem to stand it," he explained to me apologetically fifty years after Little Crow's raid. "Everywhere I looked I sort of . . ." He broke off to examine his palms as though searching for slivers. "Well, I went up to the Red River Valley on the Minnesota-Dakota border and got my start as a rancher there from 1865 to 1875."

From 1875 to 1877 Mr. Webster served as a civilian scout in the war against the Sioux-Cheyenne Confederation. He used to say with a laugh that he was the only scout in that war who laid no claim to having been present at the fight on the Little Big Horn, in June, 1876, where one squadron of the Seventh Cavalry under Colonel Custer was wiped out and another under Major Reno fought seventy hours for survival. "I never saw Custer to my knowledge," he said, "and I certainly never saw very many dead cavalrymen either in that war or in the Rebellion."

In the spring of 1878, Mr. Webster removed to Montana Territory and began his cattle-raising operations at Juniper Wells. Although he started with ordinary range stock of the period, he was the first rancher in his part of the country to switch to the new beef strains, and much of his early prosperity came from supplying pure-bred animals to other stockmen in Eastern Montana and Western Dakota.

In 1889, on a business trip to Minnesota, Mr. Webster met and married Clarissa Collingwood, an elementary school teacher of Duluth. He was forty-three years old. I do not know how old Clarissa was, and I venture the opinion that Mr. Webster did not know. She was the kind of woman who would tell no one her age, and if she did the figures would be wrong. I estimate that in 1889 she probably appeared to be about twenty-five years old and was at least thirty-five.

To preface my description of Clarissa, I must confess that I never liked her even when I was a small boy. In assessing the worth of my views, some allowance must also be made for prejudices against her which developed after I attained maturity. It is therefore significant that I remember her as always moving and speaking in a vivid, almost distinguished manner. She was a tall, slender woman with ash-colored hair, green eyes, and a thin high-bridged nose. Her features were not entirely regular, but she carried herself with the elegant beauty of a born actress. Her lightest word was enunciated as though it had been rehearsed, and even her affections were bestowed with an air of histrionics.

Perhaps this is enough to explain why Mr. Webster married Clarissa. Unconsciously he was searching for a woman who was different from the ones he had known—a small number, certainly. For twenty-four years he had been on the frontier where women of any kind were scarce and carefully classified. Squaws, dance-hall girls, and the homesteaders' daughters—these were the main categories. Something in the man's character kept him from the first two; something in his personality kept him from the third. He was the eldest child of Lucy Stewart Webster. He could not marry an Indian or a camp follower.

The women in the third group were at such a premium on the frontier that they did not need to indicate an interest in any man. They waited confidently for the attentions their scarcity commanded. In this regard they all acted alike. Thus they kept J. J. Webster from being interested in them. Unconsciously he was searching for a woman who did not act like other women.

Clarissa Collingwood apparently saw to the heart of this situation at a glance, and she moved with decision when the wealthiest rancher in Northeastern Montana came into view. She was consciously searching for financial security. She showed her interest clearly and unmistakably to this man who personified her objective. The impact on him was immediate and complete. Indeed it never left him. He had been looking for distinction. This woman had it. Even at her worst she was never commonplace. At the lowest ebb of their marital fortunes, Mr. Webster never ceased to be grateful for that circumstance.

For most of the details of their married life in the years before I observed them personally, I rely on the reminiscences of Levi Kingman as related to me on various occasions long after Clarissa had left Mr. Webster. Since I have compared Levi's report with those of the few other sources available, the following is a composite summary rather than a direct quotation.

About the time the Army killed those Sioux ghost dancers at Wounded Knee (1890), according to all sources, a man arrived in Coyote Point who had known Clarissa back in Minnesota—or somewhere. He was a big, handsome dude, to use Levi's description, about forty years old, smooth shaven, wearing fine, tailor-made clothes, a flashy diamond ring, and another big diamond in a stickpin. He wore no gun in sight but may have packed one in a shoulder holster, although most of my informants did not think so. His coat hung too smoothly for that. He probably carried a Derringer in a vest pocket or other convenient location. He did not act like a man who was totally unarmed. His name was *Peter D'Autreterre.* I got the spelling from a yellowed copy of the *Coyote Point Courier,* dated March 18, 1893, that had been treasured in Kingman's rawhide trunk throughout the years. Levi pronounced the name *Dotterer,* claiming that was the way the man himself said it.

Clarissa was in town for the week end when D'Autreterre arrived. She had come in to get the weekly mail, buy some cloth for new dresses, and go to church. She had ridden from the ranch on Friday in a buckboard driven by the new Bar-W hand, Abner Peddiwell. The boy had a list of supplies he had been commissioned by the cook to get at the general store, but otherwise he had no duties in town except to wait for the boss's wife and drive her home on Sunday afternoon. Perhaps he observed the first meeting in Coyote Point of Clarissa and D'Autreterre; if so, he mentioned it to none of my later informants.

On Friday evening, Saturday, and Sunday, there were various meetings of the two Minnesotans. They were observed in conversation in the hotel parlor. They ate their meals together in the hotel dining room. They walked out to the edge of the town and studied the course of Coyote Creek from the footbridge. On Sunday morning they attended church together. Neither of them seemed to wish to invest their meetings with a veil of even nominal secrecy. They met openly without any apparent attention to the covert intensity with which they were being watched by the entire town.

The intensity was understandable. This was Mr. Webster's wife in friendly companionship with a strange dude who appeared to have ample funds and no visible occupation. I judge that Clarissa enjoyed the situation, even though it may have revived painful memories.

Early Sunday afternoon the young Bar-W wrangler brought the buckboard and team to the hotel. When his passenger finally emerged, after a long wait, the driver stepped down beside the near front wheel to assist her to her seat, but all he did was hold the horses. D'Autreterre shouldered past him without a glance and helped Clarissa into the rig as though it were a royal coach.

Perhaps this was the first time that Abner Peddiwell and Peter D'Autreterre had seen each other at close range, if indeed the older man looked at the boy with the reins on that occasion. In the remaining five years of their lives, they probably met again not more than three or four times and then only casually.

D'Autreterre bought the small Rocker-M place north of the Hunkpapa Range. He never visited the Bar-W Ranch, but he still contrived to be in Coyote Point, fifty miles from his own territory, almost every time Clarissa spent a few days in town. My father, having been promoted from horse wrangler to a regular status, did not customarily drive Clarissa to town. Levi Kingman could remember only this one instance.

The circumstances of the last meeting between Abner Peddiwell and Peter D'Autreterre are well authenticated, though solely by physical evidence. The events of March 15, 1895, in a little pocket less than a mile west of the pack trail from Coyote Point to the Rocker-M, as reconstructed by Mr. Webster and his men, are clear. This trail, used by D'Autreterre and his hands as they came across the nearest pass and headed for town, ran ten miles east of the Peddiwell cabin. The trail at that point skirted Bar-W range, but the pasture was poor. My father seldom had occasion to ride in that direction unless he was looking for strayed stock or hunting deer.

A light snow had fallen on the evening of March 14, followed by a warm Chinook wind early the next morning. On the moist, white blanket every movement of man and animal was registered for even the most amateur tracker to read.

About the middle of the forenoon on the fifteenth, Abner Peddiwell rode up to the ridge overlooking the pocket on its western and steeper side, the side away from the trail. He dismounted before he got up on the skyline, probably to investigate the meaning of smoke he saw rising in thin wisps from the depression. He removed his Winchester from its scabbard on the saddle and tied his horse to a small tree, apparently afraid that if the animal were left only with the reins on the ground he might move a few steps onto the ridge where he could be seen from the bottom of the pocket. Young Peddiwell then crawled over the ridge and began cautiously to descend the side of the pocket, keeping himself screened by the small pines that grew here and there along the slope.

My father was about twenty yards from the fire when he stepped into the open with his rifle leveled at a man with a hot running iron in his hand bending over a hog-tied yearling steer. He disarmed the man by ordering him to unbuckle his gunbelt, letting it drop with its weapon to the ground. His prisoner was the Rocker-M foreman, a middle-aged cowhand named Myers.

Peddiwell backed Myers away from the fire and then walked forward to pick up the man's gun. As he did so he must have observed the clear evidence of guilt in the partially reconstructed brand on the prostrate animal. The bar part of the *Bar-W* had already been changed to a rocker. There remained only a blotting operation and an additional stroke at the end of the *W* to convert it into an *M*.

My father must have held his prisoner for only a minute or two when he was ordered from behind to drop his rifle. The second man was D'Autreterre. He had been acting as a lookout on the side toward the trail, had heard my father's voice, and had moved to take him from the rear.

That Abner Peddiwell was not immediately shot was probably because the Rocker-M men wanted to get him away from the branding fire and wipe out the tracks in that vicinity so that the reason for his death would not be so plainly advertised. From their standpoint he had to be killed. He was a Bar-W man of known loyalty, and he had discovered them in the process of committing what was in those days and in that country a capital crime.

The fact that the change in the brand was not completed nor the animal released indicates that the succeeding action must have taken place almost immediately. D'Autreterre fell with a knife wound at the right of his throat that severed his jugular vein. Myers dropped near the yearling with two deep cuts in his body, one under his right arm and the other directly in his heart. Young Abner Peddiwell lay alongside the foreman with a bullet hole just above his left ear, his knife still gripped in his right hand. Of the three pistols and the rifle at the scene, only one had a fired shell. This was D'Autreterre's Colt .45 which lay in the snow beside him.

Just preceding this action, D'Autreterre had apparently been guarding his prisoner while Myers had moved over to the fire to finish changing the yearling's brand. Neither the Rocker-M foreman nor his boss knew Peddiwell's custom, unusual in that part of the West, of carrying a knife in a soft leather sheath inside the top of his right boot. The overalls the young man customarily wore outside his boot tops covered the protruding hilt of the weapon. All the Bar-W hands and many other men who worked the round-ups on the Juniper Creek side of the Hunkpapas knew this peculiarity of Abner Peddiwell and passed it with little comment. The boy was a Southerner and liked to have a knife handy. Why not?

D'Autreterre and Myers died on March 15, 1895, for lack of that information. The Rocker-M boss, regarding his prisoner as completely disarmed, must have allowed his attention to shift to Myers' job of changing the brand. My father, sitting on the ground to the right of D'Autreterre, no doubt with his arms resting on his knees, was able to get a firm grip on the hilt of his knife. He leaped, struck D'Autreterre the one mortal blow, rushed Myers and cut him down before he could draw, all probably in an elapsed time of less than three seconds. At this point D'Autreterre, choking on his own blood, managed to raise his pistol, and with uncanny marksmanship, luck, or a combination of both, gave final punctuation to the fight. The bullet probably entered my father's brain just as the knife entered Myers' heart.

Two Bar-W men met Myers' horse that afternoon on the pack trail. The animal had stepped on his trailing reins, broken them, and headed for home. The Bar-W men backtracked him to pick up his thrown rider and came to the scene in the pocket. The hog-tied yearling was still alive but too weak to bawl. My father's horse whinnied anxiously behind the ridge, and D'Autreterre's mount, also tethered to a tree, answered him on the opposite slope. The record of the morning was printed in the snow.

The one other object I mentioned earlier as being a memento of my father is his boot knife. It is a slender, double-edged blade about seven inches long, hand-forged from a file, judging by marks near the leather-wrapped hilt, and tempered to take a razor-honed sharpness. It is obviously a weapon rather than a tool.

I have seldom carried this knife, except on active military service when I have never been without it, but I take it out of its sheath periodically, examine it carefully to see that it has no rust spots, rub it with a soft, oily cloth, and then put it away again. Sometimes on these occasions I have a vague feeling that I understand the North and the South just a little better than I did previously.

This is doubtless a delusion but a comforting one.

THREE

The Education of
Rain-in-the-Face

THE BIG BLACK HORSE with the white splash on his face finally lay quiet. I stood peering through the rails of the corral with an intensity I had never before felt in watching the spring horsebreaking. Perhaps it was because I was almost six years old and had therefore begun to see new details in the process. Maybe this horse responded with unusual violence to restraint, and I could now better appreciate that response in another being. Whatever the cause, I felt a compassion for the prostrate animal that moved me close to tears.

The horse was a four-year-old gelding who should have been caught in the round-up of the previous year but had eluded capture in the rough lands to the north and had thus gained an added twelve months of freedom. This morning he had felt a rope for the first time since he had been branded as a nurseling. The very touch of the manila on his neck had seemed more to infuriate than frighten him. After his first surge away from it had brought him to a choking halt, he had whirled promptly and charged Tanky Waters, the man at the other end of the rope.

Tanky had his high heels dug into the ground to brace himself and was leaning his one hundred ninety pounds against the pull. He sat down abruptly as the animal turned and came directly at him with front hooves flying for the kill. The man was in little or no danger, however, for three more ropes descended on the charging animal. One pulled the horse's head back with savage force; the other encircled his front feet and jerked them from under him. As his nose hit the ground, still another rope snaked out, caught one hind foot, and then looped twice in swift half-hitches around both hind legs.

Tanky walked over to the prostrate animal, brushing dirt from the seat of his overalls and humiliated by the general laughter. The jocular remarks were more barbed than would have been the case if Mr. Webster had been present instead of in his office at the ranch house.

"This here is a *horse*, Boy. You maybe been workin' with colts?"

"He's friendly, Tanky. He just wanted to shake hands with you, polite like."

And this in a mock aside to the foreman; "Say, Levi, probably you better get somebody who's more used to ridin' horses to ..."

"I'll ride him," Tanky bellowed. "I'll ride him into the ground!"

"You better calm down first," observed Levi Kingman drily. "You don't wanta get on that horse with any funny notions or he's liable to ride *you* into the ground and put his hoof prints on you to boot."

The horse showed unusual calm as he was blindfolded, pulled to his feet, and saddled. If I had been a little older, I might have recognized the seeming docility for the danger signal it was. No doubt Tanky and the other men knew what it meant. Certainly they went about their preparation with every sign of care, checking cinch and stirrup straps and adjusting the halter shank with meticulous attention.

The gelding was not bridled. Mr. Webster believed that a bit in a horse's mouth the first time he was ridden constituted a danger to the animal's education and the rider's neck. The unfortunate horse sometimes thus acquired the practice of falling backwards on the rider. On the Bar-W this trick, once learned, earned its possessor a permanent place among the pack animals or a bullet between the eyes.

Tanky stepped into the saddle, settled himself, and took the halter shank in his left hand and the quirt in his right.

"Let 'er go," he said grimly.

One man at the horse's head jerked off the blindfold, and the other relinquished the ear he had been gripping. As they stepped back, before Tanky had time to swing the quirt, the horse's front feet were off the ground in his first buck.

In later years I saw in action some of the greatest bucking horses of the West, including *No Name* of Pendleton, the most workmanlike performer ever to come under my observation. I realize that Tanky's mount on that March day of 1899 was not in their professional class. He lacked the finesse that only experience can give. He had the requisite weight, however, the agility, the calculating approach, and the will to win that would have put him among the major stars of the rodeo circuit, had his first bucking performance not also have been his last.

The black horse bucked straight away across the corral, then reversed almost in mid-air and bucked back again, his hind feet hitting the ground slightly after his forefeet so that each time he came down he hammered the saddle against the base of his rider's spine with all the power of his eleven hundred pounds.

As he came up to the corral fence he reversed once more and now started landing with hind feet first and front feet snapping to right and left in jarring rhythm. On the third reverse, Tanky, unable as yet to get his quirt in action, whether by accident or design, roweled the animal's shoulder.

The black horse screamed as the spur struck and moved abruptly into a run. In two jumps he was at the corral rails and cleared them like a hunter. Ahead of him was open range except for one small spot, Clarissa's flower garden at the edge of the creek. Perhaps, running blindly, he hit it by chance; more likely he headed deliberately for the sunflower stalks and surrounding fence posts that looked like a thicket in which he might remove this man from his back.

The flower-garden fence had the only barbed wire to be found on the Bar-W in 1899. Cattle had leaned across the top rail to crop at Clarissa's flowers, and she had ordered the wire. It was a secure job with three strands at eight-inch intervals on top of a five-rail stake-and-rider base. The black horse saw the rails and cleared them, but he carried the wires sawing across his chest to the ground. Tanky tried too late to leave him, but he too was caught by the wire and pinned with his left leg doubled under the horse.

Two mounted men were at the spot with swinging ropes almost as soon as the horse went down, and four dismounted men, including Mr. Webster from his office at the ranch house, converged on the flower garden soon thereafter. By the time my short legs had carried me to the garden fence, the horse was again hog-tied, with a man sitting on his head, the door of the garden-tool shed was off its hinges to serve as a stretcher for Tanky, and my hand was gripping Mr. Webster's forefinger.

It was not until I spoke that I knew I was crying.

"Is he hurt bad?" I sobbed.

One of the men lifting Tanky onto the door glanced at me curiously. "Naw," he said, "just a busted leg."

Mr. Webster knew that I was not talking about Tanky.

"I'll get in there and see," he answered me matter-of-factly, "and if he isn't hurt too bad, why, you and me, we'll fix him up."

My memory has a blank right at this point. Someone must have brought wire cutters, a basin of warm water, a bottle of carbolic acid, a big needle, and a spool of heavy, white, silk thread. The next thing I recall is that I was miraculously assisting Mr. Webster in a surgical operation, and both of us were cool and businesslike.

"It looks sort of bad, Abner, but we can fix it."

"Yes, sir, I guess we can."

"Now, the needle."

"And the thread?"

"That's right. You hold this now while I sew it up."

The flap of bloody hide was in place, and my hands held it there steadily as the surgeon took his stitches.

When the sewing was done and I could only pat the horse's neck as Mr. Webster cut and rolled up the barbed wire, I got a little sick. It was then that Mr. Webster started composing a story-song like those he sometimes made up for Jim and me at bedtime.

> We'll get him up out of the dirt,
> We'll get him up so he can run,
> We'll fix him up so he won't hurt
> We'll fix him up so he'll have fun,

he sang in confidential tones.

"Is there some more to it?" I asked delightedly.

"Yes, sir, I think there is," said Mr. Webster, "but that's all we got time for right now."

I do not know how long it was after the horse was hurt before I received the news. I would judge it was a week or less because I remember holding a box of salve to help Mr. Webster dress the cuts on the horse's breast when it happened. I suppose that before Mr. Webster made the decision he wanted to be sure that the animal was basically good-tempered and would recover from his injury.

"Abner," he said, "today is March 29, so tomorrow is your birthday."

"Yes, sir," I replied mechanically. I knew the cook would have a birthday cake for me. I had seen him baking it that afternoon.

"You've helped me a lot with this horse," continued Mr. Webster, "and I'm going to give him to you for a birthday present. I'm giving him to you a little bit before your birthday because you'll probably want to brush him up tonight so he'll look more like a birthday present tomorrow morning."

I must have stared in speechless shock.

"You've taken good care of your little burro, Jenny," Mr. Webster went on, "but now you're big enough for a real horse, and this *is* a horse."

"I'll give Jenny to Jim," I said, beginning swiftly to plan my life and that of my little brother around this wonder.

"That's good," said Mr. Webster. "Jim is pretty small yet, and Jenny will be just the right size for him."

I do not remember how long it took me to name my horse or just why, beyond the suggestion of the white splash, I called him *Rain-in-the-Face*. I had obviously heard the great war chief's name mentioned. He was still living at that time, and two years later I had the honor to be presented to him. He spoke to me courteously and complimented me on my Lacotah pronunciation.

Mr. Webster commented approvingly on my choice of name for the horse. "Rain-in-the-Face," he said. "That's a good name for a good runner and a good name for a horse with nerve too. That Hunkpapa chief traveled eighty miles mighty fast in the dead of winter after breaking out of the guardhouse, and nobody that I know ever thought he was easy to scare."

Rain-in-the-Face, the horse, had his own box stall. I suppose I groomed him first under Mr. Webster's close supervision, but I was working with him alone by the time his breast had healed. I had an apple box I used for a platform as I wielded the brush and currycomb on his glossy hide.

I do not know how Rain-in-the-Face would compare with other handsome horses if I could see him today, but he is certainly the most beautiful horse in my gallery of memories. Except for the irregular white patch across his face, something he must have inherited from a pinto in his mother's Spanish-Moorish ancestry, and a few white hairs where the stitches had been taken in his breast, he had the shining blue-black color of his German coach-horse father. He was bred for carriage stock, and if he had been rounded up as a three-year-old he would no doubt have landed on Mr. Webster's Red River Valley farm to be broken to harness.

Rain-in-the-Face was a big horse for riding purposes even on the Bar-W whose owner favored big horses for saddle work. Mr. Webster knew why he needed big horses. The purebred cattle he was raising were markedly bigger than the old range stock, and when a man dropped a loop on one of them he wanted a horse under him who could when necessary step back against the pull of a suddenly straightened rope and snap a half-ton of galloping beef to attention.

On reflection I conclude that this period when I was "gentling" Rain-in-the-Face was the happiest time of a childhood that was seldom unhappy. I lived with the horse, except for the hours I gave grudgingly to meals and sleep. I talked to him endlessly, believing implicitly that he understood every word I uttered. I measured his grain and then always added a trifle more because, as I explained to him, he was a big horse. I wrestled hay into his manger. I led him around the corral. I picked up his feet one after the other daily to inspect them. Of course, he lifted them for me. I was too small to do more than merely signal to him that I wanted to look at his feet.

This last achievement, I remember, was regarded with awe by the ranch-hands, some of whose mounts had to be thrown and hog-tied before they would submit to being shod.

The actual preparation for my first riding of Rain-in-the-Face must have been beyond my capacity, but Mr. Webster apparently guided me so skillfully that I thought I did it all myself. I have no memory of adult help or of any human witness when I first mounted the horse.

Rain-in-the-Face and I were in his stall. He was eating and I was standing on the apple box to brush him. I put my arms over his withers, as I had often done before, but this time I pulled myself on my stomach across his back, swung a leg over, and sat up. He turned his head, a little surprised, and nuzzled my foot. I patted him and explained the situation. I said that he was a big horse, that he was my horse, and that I had to learn to ride him. I pointed also to the fact that I was two years his senior.

Whether Rain-in-the-Face understood my words, I am not prepared to testify. A year later he seemed to know Lacotah as well as English, and he may not have known one from the other.

That he comprehended the full social import of my speech, no matter what the language, I had then and have today no slightest doubt.

Measured by certain standards of intellectual performance that men usually apply to dogs, chimpanzees, white rats, and human beings, no horse is very intelligent. Some of them, like some dogs, chimpanzees, rats, and men, are extraordinarily stupid.

In certain kinds of social intelligence, which men and chimpanzees do not rate very high because they commonly lack it, and which dogs conceal under servile flattery of their human associates, a good horse is markedly superior. Consider the keen observation that enables a trick horse to catch cues so slight as to be imperceptible even to the man who gives them. Consider the horse sense which enables the animal to know as soon as he sees a stranger, not to mention a man with whom he is acquainted, the state of the person's mental health and the extent to which he is angry, frightened, or otherwise disturbed.

Rain-in-the-Face had this special sense in full measure. In a week I was riding him everywhere on the ranch. At first he sometimes stiffened and pulled himself together for a jump when he was startled. I always stopped him and gave him my standard lecture. I told him over and over again that he had to let me ride him.

"I know you can throw me, Rain-in-the-Face," I said earnestly. "You can throw a grown man; I think you can throw any man in the world; but you mustn't throw me."

Rain-in-the-Face must have listened to, understood, and agreed with my argument. He never threw me.

Perhaps this is one reason why I still believe that the lecture technique can be very successful under proper conditions.

The first condition is that the class understand the lecturer on a horse-sense level.

FOUR

Pre-school Interlude

M R . W E B S T E R bought ranches and farms more often than he sold them, and he made money on them in good times and did not lose much if any money on them in bad times. He started in 1865 with the proceeds of the sale of the 160-acre homestead in Southern Minnesota. He bought the Red River Valley farm of 640 acres, paid for it in ten years, and later expanded it to 800 acres. In his service against the Sioux-Cheyenne Confederation he located the Juniper Wells range in Montana. In the period from 1877 to 1900 he made the Bar-W the outstanding horse and cattle ranch of its region.

In 1899 Mr. Webster started another ranch in the Ochoco Valley of Central Oregon. By 1915, when Jim was twenty and I was twenty-two, the J. J. Webster interests included the Red River Valley farm in Minnesota, the Bar-W Ranch in Montana, the Jay-Jay Ranch in Oregon, the Webster apple orchards near Hood River, Oregon, and Wenatchee, Washington, about two thousand acres of wheat land divided between the John Day and Umatilla Valleys in Oregon, and extensive timber holdings on the west slope of the Coast Range near Tilamook, Oregon.

There was no magic in Mr. Webster's economic success. He was a man of strong intelligence, constructive imagination, and driving energy who had nothing much to engage his talents except the expanding Northwest. He was certainly not much concerned with money. As executor of his estate, I can testify in this connection to facts that no one person other than Mr. Webster himself knew prior to his death. Year after year, persistently but unostentatiously, he gave more than half his income to schools, colleges, hospitals, and churches. He used most of the remainder to expand his holdings.

Just before Mr. Webster's death he was directing his attention to the Peace River country in Canada. Had he lived a few more years, I believe he might have acquired a substantial tract of land there, and the Peace River Valley might have been more developed and therefore more prosperous than it is today.

I have already given my guesses as to why a man of this capacity should have married Clarissa Collingwood. Now that I must describe the final breach between these two people, I see that I need to give some additional facts that may or may not support those guesses.

Mr. Webster's most important teacher was probably his mother; she had taught in rural schools in Massachusetts for three years before her marriage. James Jonathan himself attended a country school in Vermont for three or four months each winter from his sixth to his ninth year. In that time he probably learned about all the fundamentals the institution had to offer.

Thereafter Mr. Webster had no formal schooling. For the life he lived, he was not much if at all handicapped by this lack, but he believed that he was greatly handicapped. He yearned for intellectual achievement, not for himself—he deemed that impossible—but for his people, his sons, his community, his country, and—his wife.

Like many relatively unschooled men of his generation, Mr. Webster overestimated the importance of schooling. He tended to confuse it with the much larger field of education. He regarded school teaching, furthermore, as a social enterprise of paramount worth. In spite of these misconceptions—if indeed they be such —he made judgments about the nature and purposes of schooling that would have done credit to highly placed educators had they been competent to reach similar conclusions.

Mr. Webster's speech supporting the proposal to establish a high school in the county seat nearest the Jay-Jay Ranch stated his views on education.

"I hear the talk about what this town needs," he said, "and it sounds like good sense to me, but maybe it's not all of the sense we have to have in this thing." He started hesitatingly and mildly as always but moved directly to the heart of the question in his first sentence. "The boys who have just spoken have told us that the town needs electric lights, a better water system, paved streets, and improved fire-fighting equipment as much or more than it needs the new high school. 'Where are we going to get the money to pay for all these things we need?' some of them have asked. 'We've already got more taxes than we can bear,' they tell us.

"You all know I'm not posted very well on schooling. I never had very much of it, as anybody can see." Here the old man dropped the hat he had been twisting nervously in his heavy hands, straightened his shoulders, and measured his words.

"But I don't have to be a scholar, Mr. Chairman; I don't have to have very much schooling; I don't even have to be very bright to tell you what I got on my mind about what this town needs. This town needs better and smarter folks, and the only practical way I know to get 'em is to educate 'em up to it."

His final sentence rolled out with each word cracking like a pistol shot. I have never seen an audience so powerfully affected by a speech. Men who had been arguing against the proposal listened with shining eyes and then walked up to the ballot box in that meeting and voted for the new high school. In the more than half century since that speech, the community in which it was delivered has never recovered from it. Its virus is so deep in the veins of that town that most of the citizens do not want to recover from it.

I am convinced that if today there were only five hundred men like J. J. Webster scattered over the United States in positions comparable to those which he occupied in his era, there would be a national revolution in the support of public education.

Mr. Webster's appreciation of educational institutions and processes was really the outward expression of an inner search for the instruments and measures of intellectual quality that he did not know how to embody except in terms of the school.

It might have been predicted, therefore, when the nineteen-year-old sergeant of infantry took his honorable discharge in 1865, that in the succeeding quarter century on the rough edges of the expanding nation he would not marry an ordinary woman, no matter how superficially attractive she might seem on the frontier. She had to carry with her something he could at least mistake for intellectual quality.

When Mr. Webster visited St. Paul in November, 1889, it was the first time he had been there since his part of the world had begun to regard him as markedly successful. It was probably inevitable that now he would meet women shrewd enough to assess his quest for a wife and try to satisfy it.

He met at least one such woman. Clarissa Collingwood, first on her Thanksgiving vacation in St. Paul, and then on Mr. Webster's last visit to Duluth, and finally in St. Paul again, played the correct role to the hilt. When the curtain rose on their meetings she undoubtedly took the charming, amiable, suave, and intellectually distinguished part for which her intuition furnished the script.

My respect for the man who married Clarissa on Christmas Eve, 1889, compels me to add that it would be a mistake to think that she lacked intellectual quality. She had plenty of it, far more than most women I have known, and I have lived for many years in university communities where women of highest intellectual abilities are commonplace. Clarissa Collingwood was only a graduate of a little normal school, but she knew how to act the part of a blue stocking.

Thus, so far as Mr. Webster was concerned, when Clarissa came to the Indies which he envisioned, she carried the wealth of the Indies with her. That she had a wide streak of poverty in her character was not so much a fault that she contributed to the marriage as it was a defect in Mr. Webster's specifications for a wife.

From the time I came to the Bar-W at the age of two until I started to school on the Reservation at the age of six, I saw Clarissa almost every day. I cannot say that I ever developed the slightest affection for her or that she ever displayed any interest in me, affectionate or otherwise. Occasionally she patted Jim's head. She never touched me that I can remember.

The cook fed and clothed Jim and me. Mr. Webster played with us before bedtime and sang or recited the long stories that were his principal resources for the entertainment of children. Jim and I played with each other and with our puppies, kittens, calves, and saddle mounts. Clarissa curled her hair, read all the books written by Mrs. E. D. E. N. Southworth, and went to Coyote Point almost every weekend to shop and attend church.

If the death of D'Autreterre at the hands of a Bar-W man left any scars on Clarissa, she never showed them for a child to see.

At this moment it seems startling that in the many years since my father, D'Autreterre, and Myers died almost simultaneously I have never before thought of a certain possibility. Just now it occurs to me that perhaps Clarissa did not wish to touch me because I was the child of the man who had killed her lover. On careful reflection, however, I reject this possibility. Clarissa had too much intellectual toughness to be guided in her gestures by a fancy of that kind. She did not touch me because she did not see such an act as part of her role. It was as simple as that.

I do not know why the final break between Clarissa and Mr. Webster came in 1899. I hasten to add that this break was not accompanied by a divorce. So far as I could determine by examination of Mr. Webster's personal papers, Clarissa was his wife at the time of his death, if she was alive herself. I cannot imagine Mr. Webster taking steps to divorce her. I do not believe, furthermore, that she would have willingly cut herself off from as much money as was involved in being the wife of Mr. Webster, unless she could have acquired a wealthier husband by so doing.

In 1912, when Jim left for college, Clarissa disappeared from St. Paul. Up to that date she had received a very generous monthly allowance from Mr. Webster. I assume that when his

checks began to be returned with indications that Clarissa had
left St. Paul without giving the postal clerks a forwarding address, he made every effort through detective agencies to find her.
When he died, I put two agencies on her trail, but they never
traced her beyond St. Paul in 1912.

Levi Kingman was a chief source of the relatively small
amount of information that I ever had about Clarissa. He was
undoubtedly a prejudiced witness.

"She was the coolest damn' customer ever I see," he remarked to me twenty years after the event. "The night before she
pulled out for St. Paul with little Jim, she come into the ranch
office where I was helpin' the boss go over some tally books. I got
up to leave, but she set me down again. 'Mr. Webster,' she says,
'I'll want a buckboard early in the mornin' to catch the noon
train east at the Point.'

" 'All right,' says Mr. Webster, 'and when will you be back?'

" 'I won't be back,' she says, '—ever,' and then she swishes
outa the room like she was on casters—the smoothest walkin'
woman I ever see anywheres.

"Mr. Webster never said nothin' for quite a spell. He just
looked older and grayer as he set there starin' at the tally books.
Finally he kinda hunched his shoulders up and says, 'Let's see,
Levi, what's next?' For a second, I was mixed up. I thought he
was talkin' about *her*. Then I suddenly got it through my thick
head that he wanted to go on checkin' them God-damn' tally
books."

FIVE

Medicine Horse

THE CLOSE FRIENDSHIP between Mr. Webster and Medicine Horse was begun in 1877 when the Lacotah Sioux were being put back on the reservation after the war. It lasted for forty years, strengthened by every contact between the two men, and ended only by death.

The circumstance of my attendance at the school on the reservation forty miles from Coyote Point beginning in the fall of 1899 came primarily from that friendship.

I went to a one-room rural school for six years with about fifty Lacotah children. In that period I progressed through the eight grades. I saw Mr. Webster intermittently. In summer vacations I rode Rain-in-the-Face and led my pinto packhorse, Spotted Robe, to the Bar-W at Juniper Wells for long visits with Levi Kingman. When school was in session, I lived on the Reservation in the house of the white teacher, Miss Margaret Abernathy. I learned to speak Lacotah as a child of that age acquires any language he hears. I played with the Indian boys, particularly my special buddy, Sky Bow, grandson of Medicine Horse.

All these and related experiences in those six years were educational, yet I doubt that their combined effects on me in the development of persistent attitudes and the production of permanent behavior changes were as great as the impact of a relatively few, mostly casual contacts with one man.

That man was Medicine Horse.

Who was he? To Miss Abernathy he was an illiterate savage. To the Indian agent he was a notorious former "hostile." To the missionaries he was an inconvertible pagan. In the relationships between him and these representatives of the Pale Eyes' culture, candor compels me to add, the weight of educated understanding, love for former enemies, and tolerance for other religions, was overwhelmingly on his side.

To me Medicine Horse was first of all a chief. That was what Holly Woman, his wife, called him every time she addressed him formally. She seldom spoke to him informally in my hearing, and then it appeared to be a low-voiced comment on some private joke between them.

Medicine Horse was also a priest of Wakan Tanka, the Great Mystery, the Supreme Being of the monotheistic Plains Indians. As a priest and as a man, he had the characteristics of gentle goodness which seem so easy for the Pale Eyes to preach and so hard for them to practice.

Finally and above all, Medicine Horse was a teacher.

Mr. Webster presented me to the chief the first morning after we arrived. I carried a new carbine across my saddle as my introductory gift to the chief. As we rode up the hill toward his teepee, Mr. Webster was giving me final instructions on the protocol of the coming interview.

"Don't be fooled by his almost sleepy way of looking at you," he said. "That's a polite way. That's the way you're supposed to look at people if you're somebody like Sunka Wakan Wakan." I had already noted Mr. Webster's tendency to use Lacotah expressions as soon as we crossed the Reservation line, as now when he gave the sonorous original of Medicine Horse's name.

"I will talk in Lacotah first," Mr. Webster continued his briefing, "and you just look down at the ground. Then I'll put the carbine, boot and all, in your hands. You lift it up above your shoulders, slow, like this, and then you look right in his eyes. You need to do that because he will want to see if you have *wakan* in your eyes. When he takes the gun and starts to speak, you look right down at the ground again."

I had no difficulty in following these instructions although I kept wanting to look longer at the slender chief. When I held the carbine up and looked into his face, he smiled suddenly. Without knowing what *wakan* was, I remember a triumphant thought that he had found it in my eyes.

From the time I first saw the chief at the teepee entrance until Mr. Webster and I had mounted, raised our right hands in the Plains salute, and ridden down the hill towards the river, Medicine Horse filled my spirit with his presence. Every other time I saw him, he achieved the same *wakan* result. (I have crossed the Reservation line again myself and so I cannot translate *wakan*).

It could not have been just the man's appearance that had this effect on me. For example, he dressed very simply. Blue denim trousers and shirt, moccasins, and in cold weather, a plain blanket were the main elements of his wardrobe. I never saw him wear a coat or a hat of any kind. He, (or rather Holly Woman for him), kept his hair in two braids that hung forward over his shoulders, ending at his waist. Except for the beadwork on his moccasins and belt and the buckskin thongs at the ends of his braids, his dress was unornamented, even plain.

It was not because of the chief's size or any other physical trait, moreover, that he was impressive. He stood less than five and one-half feet in his moccasins, and he never weighed more than 120 pounds. Neither did he exercise any of the tricks of personal charm or dominance by which some men make themselves remembered. He spoke quietly, almost hesitantly. He had none of the "haughty-bearing" or "piercing-glance" mannerisms which I was later embarrassedly to encounter in dime-novel "descriptions" of Indian chiefs. In conversation he looked at you only occasionally in fleeting inquiry or appreciation. In any group of more than two or three, he seldom spoke at all and then only in response to repeated invitation.

Now that I have tried to sketch the chief's manner and appearance, claiming that they were not outwardly impressive, I see that the picture is hazy and inaccurate. Every line of Medicine Horse's face, every movement of his hands, and every intonation of his voice heightened the attention and sensibility of his observers and hearers. None of this, I think, was art. It was an expression of the inner man.

The man was impressive because he was always different in his own individual way, and he was different for what were emphatically *his* reasons. He never wore a war bonnet, for instance; the practice did not fit his personal *wakan,* his unique spirit. He never counted *coups* or thought enough of the custom to offer an explanation for his aversion to it. In a society where polygamy was the mark of success, he rejected it for himself in his own inimitable manner.

Holly Woman was Medicine Horse's biographer to Sky Bow and me. No great man ever had a more charming interpreter. She was at her best and proudest when she told of the chief's decision to have only one wife. I give the essence of her story as well as I can remember and translate its delicate, Lacotah-woman's style of speech into this language which, though claimed by its speakers to be now the greatest world tongue, is ill fitted for the discussion of truly *wakan* matters.

"Sunka Wakan Wakan," she said, "struck his first *coup* when he was sixteen. He unhorsed a Crow chief with a wrestling magic. They were trying to raid our camp, and these, my own eyes, saw the fight. I was afraid for Sunka Wakan Wakan then, for he was only a boy and he seemed so small against that big, ugly Crow. Their knives flashed as they came together, and then suddenly the Crow was on the ground and Sunka Wakan Wakan's whip was across the enemy's back. 'Put him in women's clothes,' he cried as he quirted the man toward the Crow warriors. 'Perhaps he can learn to cook; he cannot fight.'

"I was proud when he offered my father five good horses and a Walker pistol that fired six times," she continued, not being so immodest, of course, as to imply directly that the gifts to her father were in the nature of payment for her hand. Actually, a Lacotah woman was not bought from her father any more than a woman in our own cultural *ambiente* is bought by giving her a wedding ring. The Lacotah girl was courted, and when she gave her consent to marriage, her prospective husband gave wedding gifts to her father. The Pale Eyes, especially the priests, preachers, and traders, for their own specious reasons, always put as commercial an interpretation on Indian marriages as their imaginations could supply.

I knew this feature of the Plains culture, and I ventured to ask Holly Woman about Medicine Horse's courting of her.

"But the Chief, my Almost-Mother," I inquired, "he spoke to you about marriage first, didn't he?"

She giggled archly. "Well, of course, he was not a chief then," she said, "although he was an important warrior. He caught me a few times when I was going to the spring to get water. I did not try too hard to get away. I knew he was so gentle that he would not really hold me if I actually ran. One time he did throw his blanket over my head, and he said, under the blanket, 'I do not know how to make a flute, Holly Woman, and I do not think I could learn to play one, but I have five fast horses and a pretty good Walker pistol.' "

"And what did you say to that, my Real-Mother?" asked Sky Bow.

Holly Woman giggled again and then answered primly, *"That* is my *wakan* to me alone."

"When Sunka Wakan Wakan was elected chief of the Dog Warriors," she continued, "he was only twenty-two years old, but he was already an important man with a very good name. By this time we had been married four years, and we had no children.

"Some of the younger women began to make jokes at me about my being too jealous to let my husband marry another wife. A chief of the Dog Warriors with as many horses as he owned could have had three or four wives and perhaps five or six children. Some of the jokes were not laughing jokes, and two or three of those girls who made the jokes would have been very glad to be second or third wives of Sunka Wakan Wakan.

"I laughed as well as I could, but there came a time when I

had to speak about it to Sunka Wakan Wakan. I was ashamed to mention it to him, but I knew it must be done, so I came to him after he had eaten. 'Have you thought of marrying another wife, Chief?' I asked him.

"He was very surprised. 'Do you need help with the women's work?' he asked quickly.

" 'No, Chief,' I said. I was a strong girl.

" 'Then I do not need another wife,' he said.

" 'But, Chief,' I said—and now I was really ashamed to speak of such a thing to a man, 'I have no children, and we have been married four years. A man like you should have a son or a daughter, at least.'

"Now it was my turn to be surprised. 'Do you want to have a child, Holly Woman?' he asked me.

" 'Yes, of course, Chief,' I said, 'if I could.'

" 'Then I will pray for a child for you,' he said.

"In my astonishment, I forgot to be ashamed. 'Why, *that* is a *woman's* prayer,' I cried.

"He laughed and came the closest I ever heard him come to counting a *coup*. '*Not* if *I* make it,' he said."

Holly Woman paused and then added softly, speaking directly to Sky Bow, "Your father was born the next year."

As a teacher, Medicine Horse was an artist of great skill. Few men who ever taught me in the classroom even came near his level. As one who has long been a professional student of the learning process, I should be able to analyze his skill. What were its main elements?

You had first of all as you came under the instruction of Sunka Wakan Wakan a certainty that he was completely sincere. He never spoke satirically, sarcastically, or with hidden meanings. He laid all his intellectual, emotional, and moral cards on the table, face up. He taught Sky Bow and me because he wanted us to be good men, no matter what else might befall us. We *must* be good men, that was the number-one objective. He told us of this objective every time he gave us any instruction.

It is difficult to explain why a teacher in our schools or colleges who keeps repeating some simple objective like, "We want you to be good citizens," soon becomes a bore to whom students pay little or no attention, while an illiterate savage could say over and over again, "I tell you these old stories, my sons, to show you how to be good men, good for your people, and if I tire you please be patient with me, for I am not very bright," and get nothing but the most respectful, rapt attention from his pupils.

It is too easy to shrug the whole problem aside by saying that Medicine Horse was a great man. That says nothing. Why was he great? Great men, furthermore, are not necessarily good teachers. Some of them, indeed, are very poor teachers.

I suspect that the elements of any great teacher's skill are few and simple but so profoundly amalgamated in his total personality as almost to defy dissection. I will attempt to indicate some of them, however, in the case of Medicine Horse.

There was the simple sincerity that I have already mentioned. Perhaps the teachers who bore their students by pious recital of noble objectives do not themselves believe those objectives. Perhaps young human learners still retain enough kinship with horses to sense with automatic precision anything less than one-hundred-per-cent sincerity and at the same time to recognize the real article whenever it appears.

Sunka Wakan Wakan was not an orator, either by Lacotah or white men's standards, but when he spoke to you he laid his thoughts and feelings before you with an ease and a grace that few orators ever attain. You saw at once that his thoughts were as straight as a lance and his feelings as humane as the love of Wakan Tanka for all men.

The second crucial element in Medicine Horse's teaching was the perfection of his timing. He had no curriculum or schedule of classes to consider. He could study his pupils in their daily lives, watch their activities, observe the learning conditions under which they operated, and then make his educational play at the optimum moment.

Was it wild-plum-picking time for the women and children? The chief had a story for us about a Crow attack on plum pickers

and a twelve-year-old Lacotah boy who traveled the equivalent of
two days journey in one night to bring help from a friendly Cheyenne camp. Were we training our horses to lie down at signal? Our
teacher told us how Reno's men in the Little Big Horn fight had
trouble on that account with their single-mounts and pack animals. Did we show fear in some minor emergency? Medicine
Horse consoled us by telling how frightened he was when he was
sent to warn the white miners that they must get out of the Black
Hills.

"When I saw their cooking fire near to where they were digging in the creek bed for the heavy, yellow sand," he explained,
"I knew what I must do, but my stomach was heavy and my back
was cold. I stripped to breechclout and moccasins and likewise I
stripped my horse of his saddle. Then I painted both of us in
peace colors, but I was still much afraid, for I knew that some
white men cannot read the meaning of paint. When I took my
ceremonial lance in hand, mounted, and started for the Pale Eyes'
camp, I was not a warrior-herald. I was only a frightened child."

It is now well over a half century since I heard the slender,
soft-spoken priest of Wakan Tanka tell that story, but I can still
see more clearly than I can recall any photographic aid to learning the picture of the seventeen-year-old messenger riding slowly
into the miners' camp. As he stood up on his horse and delivered
the warning of the Sioux-Cheyenne Confederation, the white men
pulled the hammers back on their rifles and cursed him loudly.
He did not report this, of course, but I knew the talk and actions
of white men and I could imagine vividly how they reacted to this
painted, young buck on a wild-looking pinto horse.

"Get outa here, you red bastard, before I blow you off that
crow-bait."

"Never mind that jabber. Vamoose pronto."

"Get a move on, you greasy son of a bitch."

But now the boy was not frightened. He had something to
do, and that something was his duty—which is to say, in Medicine Horse's terms, it was something he was doing for his people,
something they needed to have done, something they would honor

him for doing. Now it would have been difficult for him to be frightened.

He finished his peaceful message and waited courteously for a reply. Surely someone in this camp of Pale Eyes could understand and speak the People's tongue. But the miners merely heightened their cursing, and one of them started toward him with rifle centered on the boy's chest.

Then, slowly, deliberately, Medicine Horse completed the message.

"And if you do not heed the words of our people, if you keep on digging here in this our *wakan* country against the promise made to us by the great chief of your people in the *wakan*-talking leaves he sent us, then we Lacotah and our friends, the Spotted-Horses People, will change our paint. We will ride no more to you as peaceful heralds but we will come to you with *war!*"

At the last word the boy struck his lance quivering into the ground before his horse's nose. Then, slowly, he slid down again astride the animal, leaned forward, and retrieved the lance. Still slowly, with hackamore rein, he signaled the horse to turn and held him down to a walk as he rode away. Even now I can feel the menace of those .44-40- and .45-70-caliber muzzles in the small of my own back.

Perhaps this is enough to explain why I have always been skeptical of those enthusiasts who are fond of claiming that in education one picture is worth a thousand words. There are always questions to ask at that point, like, "What picture?" and "Whose words?" In my educational development, no pictures of which I can conceive could balance Medicine Horse's, *"Now* I was not afraid; I had something to do for my people."

This particular teaching probably has an element in it that explains my disbelief in the universal application of the cliché, "The soldier who tells you that he is not always afraid in battle is lying." I have seldom been frightened in military action, and I am not by nature a brave person. I am almost always frightened before a battle begins, and I am usually frightened after it ends, but in the actual course of the battle I am so concerned with what

I have to do for my regiment or some other symbol of my people that I have no time for fear. I was a pupil of Sunka Wakan Wakan.

Although the chief never counted his coups or wore a war bonnet, he had himself great admiration for military courage. When speaking of the events of June 25 and 26, 1876, when the Sioux-Cheyenne forces clashed with the Seventh United States Cavalry, he spoke with appreciation of the courage of others than himself. He would not mention his own considerable part in that action except when prodded into it, and then he always played it down.

He had led his dog warriors into contact with Colonel Custer's squadron, pretending to be a hunting party and fleeing in apparent confusion before the attacking troopers. "That was nothing," he would say. "They fired at us with pistols and with those carbines that had cartridges that stuck in the breeches after the first round, and they hit practically nobody. We kept just out of range and led them down to where the main body of our warriors could reach them."

He always shifted his auditors' attention as soon as possible to the four men whom he regarded as the bravest of the brave in that battle, the Cheyenne warriors who advanced on foot against Captain Benteen's command, singing their death songs and calling at the end of each stanza, "This is a good day to die!" They caused Benteen to dismount his troopers and put them in skirmish formation. The resultant delay permitted the Indian women and children to get out of the camp and reach the high ground across the Little Big Horn.

"They were the bravest men in that fight," Medicine Horse would say, and then he would add, "and the next bravest man was that white soldier with three stripes on his sleeve who fought so long behind his dead horse to keep us from coming up on his friends." (Sergeant John Baker received no more honorable citation from any source.)

Holly Woman, who saw almost all phases of the battle from a point on the ridge across the river, had her own ideas about the affair. I remember her saying once to Sky Bow and me, after Medicine Horse had been telling us the Little Big Horn story, "The bravest man in that fight was a Lacotah. He was the chief of the dog warriors."

Medicine Horse spoke so gravely that at first I thought he was angry. "Holly Woman," he asked, "are you helping me teach these boys?"

"No, Great Chief," she said smoothly, and now I could see that she knew Medicine Horse was not angry. "I was just talking woman-talk to them." Then she walked away to her cooking fire with merely a hint of her ready giggle.

One day in the eighth grade, after we had been studying the Battle of Shiloh, I asked Miss Abernathy if we might study the Battle of the Little Big Horn. "There are quite a few men here on the reservation who fought in it," I said.

Miss Abernathy's hatchet face grew suddenly sharper. "Oh, you mean the Custer Massacre," she said. "Certainly not." That night at dinner in her house, with no Indians around, she pointed out the error of my ways and intimated that I would never amount to anything unless I always remembered that I was white and these savages were not to be trusted.

When Medicine Horse learned in the fall of 1917 that Sky Bow and I were both in France and in the same division (someone probably interpreted *division* as *war party* for him), he gave away two good horses to poor widow women in honor of his son and almost-son going on the warpath. Then he rode to the courthouse at Coyote Point to enlist in the United States Army. The recruiting sergeant was much better educated than Miss Abernathy, although I do not know the extent of his schooling.

"This is Medicine Horse. He is an important chief of the old days," said the Lacotah recruit who was acting as interpreter. "He wants to join up."

"How old is he?" asked the sergeant.

"How old are you, Chief," the interpreter in turn inquired of Medicine Horse.

"How old do the soldiers have to be?" asked the chief.

"They must be seventeen and not over thirty-five."

The chief struggled with his conscience. Finally, he admitted, "I am more than seventeen years old; I have been thirty-five for several winter counts. Tell the soldier that I am a pretty good tracker."

The recruiting sergeant was a diplomat. He described the dangers of a German invasion. In such a case, he pointed out, the older men would be needed to protect the women and children until the dog and fox warriors could make contact with the enemy in decisive battles. At the end, Medicine Horse shook hands with him and the interpreter, mounted, and rode back to the Reservation.

I can imagine the chief coming into the teepee when he returned, reaching for his medicine pouch as he made the usual formal request, "With your permission, Holly Woman," receiving his wife's grave consent, and then going out on the hill to pray to Wakan Tanka that he might be allowed in some way once more to strike a coup for his people.

In the spring of 1905, Sky Bow and I completed the eighth grade. Miss Abernathy gave us our certificates. I put mine carefully in my bedroll the next morning as I made my pack for the annual summer journey to the Bar-W. Then I rode slowly up the hill back of the schoolhouse to tell Sky Bow, Holly Woman, and Medicine Horse good-bye.

We exchanged gifts. Sky Bow gave me a lariat he had braided with hair from the tails of black horses. Even Rain-in-the-Face had contributed to that work of art. Sky Bow had been laboring on it most of the winter. I felt like crying as he came out and tied it with one of the shawl straps to my saddle. I gave him a slide-rule with its instruction book. He had never seen one, but he had heard of them. He had great interest in figures. In his usual fashion, he said nothing but looked his thanks while I was repeating in Pale Eyes' manner and language, "I am sure much obliged for this rope."

To Holly Woman I presented a cuckoo clock I had ordered a month earlier from Montgomery Ward. She had only an old alarm clock which required more and more frequent kerosene baths to make it run even erratically. I hung the new timepiece from a teepee pole at the foot of her bed, showed her how to wind it, adjusted the weights, and set the hands. Then we waited for the hour, and at last it came. The door opened. The bird emerged and spoke the correct number of times. Holly Woman listened and watched with shining eyes. Medicine Horse looked on with obvious delight. The woman was pleased with the fine thing her almost-son had given her. Her husband was pleased to see her happy.

Holly Woman was one of the few very beautiful women I have ever seen. She was more than fifty years old in 1905, and her beauty was of course mostly in her eyes, her manner, and her style of speech. For that matter, where else does beauty reside at any age? She pressed a new pair of beaded moccasins into my hands, and I kissed her warmly on both cheeks to show that I was white and that I loved her.

Then I pulled from the top of Spotted Robe's packsaddle my *chef d'oeuvre,* the gift for my great teacher himself. It was really in the nature of a graduation thesis, although at the age of twelve I am certain that I had never heard that term.

Two years earlier I had seen a winter robe that belonged to an elderly Cheyenne visitor. Medicine Horse had explained the rich detail of the document to Sky Bow and me. Then, with the help and advice of Dr. George Winters, the agency physician, who was a member of the state historical societies in Minnesota and Missouri, I had borrowed books which contained reproductions of winter robes. Now, after months of anxious concern and, I am sorry to add, a relatively poor technique in draftsmanship, I had a packet of drawing-paper sheets on which I had copied the robes in water colors. Why water colors? I do not know. Perhaps I merely found the water-color page in the Montgomery Ward catalogue first.

It occurs to me that just as some white men did not know the meaning of the Plains Indians' peace and war paints in the 1870's, there may be some of my Pale-Eyed readers today who do not know what a winter robe is. It is a history or rather a chronicle of winter counts. It lists in picture writing, year by year, the main events in the life of a tribe as recorded by the particular historian.

This was my gift to the chief. To see his appreciation was a delightful experience. He said nothing, of course, until he had looked long at each sheet. Then, to one who did not know him and his culture, what he did say might have seemed so brief as to imply a lack of gratitude, but I received its full import.

"This is a *wakan* thing you have done," he said, and I saw the *wakan* in his eyes as he said it. Then he turned to his bed and took from the war-bag at its head a roll of carefully tanned buckskin. Fifty years earlier it would have been buffalo hide. He lifted the roll up to me in the formal gesture of giving. I took it and unrolled it. It was a winter robe he had made for me!

I studied the document with care. It began with the year 1854, as I soon discovered by counting back from events whose dates I knew, as for example the Wagon Box fight. The chief was born in 1854, but true to his policy of never counting his own coups, the robe bore his name only once. It was in the signature position at the top where the tiny dancing horse attested his *wakan* character. I said nothing at the end but only put my hand over his signature and then went out to mount and give the parting sign.

SIX

Dr. Brown's Academy

THE REAL NAME of the school was the Tum-a-Lum Academy, but when you saw the principal, the Reverend Henry Liberty Brown, you soon recognized that the popular name for the institution was the correct one. Although the academy was the preparatory school for the University of the West, the university authorities did not run it. Dr. Brown ran it. He hired and sometimes fired the teachers. He determined the curriculum and the schedule of classes. He created the intellectual and social environment, and he modified it whenever it appeared to him to need change.

In present-day parlance, Dr. Brown was the administrator of the institution, but in those days he was the *principal teacher*. He pointed this out to us himself. He had some prejudice against the term *head master,* commonly used in other private secondary schools. Any prospective client of the academy who inadvertently called him by that title was coldly set aright. Perhaps the old gentleman's middle name and a certain general dislike for British ways were historically associated in his family.

Henricus Libertas, as the pupils called him, not of course in his presence, taught four main subjects; Latin, Greek, English poetry, and manners. The two latter disciplines were taught incidentally but if anything more thoroughly than the regularly scheduled Latin and Greek. Lest I seem to be speaking in riddles, I give a more detailed description.

For instance, the principal is teaching a class in Julius Caesar's *De Bello Gallico*.

"In what case is *polliciationibus* here, Peddiwell?" he demands abruptly as some other boy finishes translating a passage.

"The dative, sir," I perhaps answer promptly and inaccurately.

"Did you study Chapter IX of Allen and Greenough's *Grammar?*"

"No, sir, not recently."

"Then how do you expect to know what these constructions are? How do you expect to amount to anything of consequence when you do not study what you are told to study? You are learning Latin to exercise your mental faculties, and even more importantly to train your moral faculties. This is the way you do it. *Not recently!* It is no wonder to me that this country is going to perdition on a downhill road."

We studied Caesar's commentaries in the second year of the Academy; I was therefore fourteen years old at the time of this lecture. Boys of that age in a school of that kind, at least in those days, were consummate hypocrites. I sat, looking chastened because that was the way I was supposed to look, but actually I was enjoying the old man's eloquence. The rest of the class also looked chastened and also enjoyed his eloquence as he thundered on and on. After a time, however, his heart would be touched by our humble and contrite appearance, and he would change his tone and start teaching his incidental and more important subjects.

"But I do not wish to make too much of an issue of a minor matter here and speak of an academic fault as though it were a crime. At the most, not to know that *polliciationibus* here is in the ablative is merely a scholarly misdemeanor. Permit me to end this disquisition, therefore, by saying:

> I hold it truth with him who sings
> To one clear harp in divers tones
> That men may rise on stepping stones
> Of their dead selves to higher things."

At this point the old man never said, "From Tennyson's *In Memoriam*," as the teacher in the regularly scheduled class in English Literature would have had to say, according to the unwritten laws under which the teachers operated. But because Dr. Brown was not teaching English poetry officially and was merely talking as one cultivated person to another, he never insulted us by such academic citations. We worked those out ourselves, sometimes with long discussions and detailed searching of Bartlett's *Quotations*, Palgrave's *Golden Treasury*, and various collected poems. I studied these works more conscientiously than I did Allen and Greenough's *Grammar* for the precise reason that they were not required in connection with an official subject.

Sometimes Henricus Libertas made the transition from an official to an incidental subject more suddenly and pleasantly. "Why did you put *vallum* in the dative?" he might ask some luckless youth who had just written a "composition" sentence on the blackboard.

"Because, sir," the pupil could reply glibly, "the verb here is *circumspicere*."

"And what is the connection between those two circumstances, Peddiwell?" the teacher might then demand, abruptly turning toward where I was standing and sadly staring out of the window at the Willamette Valley winter rain falling determinedly on the Douglas fir branches.

"Well, sir, there is a rule about that."

"Do you know the rule?"

"I believe I do."

"Very well, let's hear it."

"Verbs compounded with *a, ab, ante, con, in, inter, ob, post, prae, pro, sub, super,* and sometimes with *circum* take the dative," I would recite triumphantly, ending with an oratorical emphasis on the final word.

"Ah, yes," the principal teacher might then say, "but one must note the qualifying adverb, *sometimes,* and this particular time is not one of those sometimes."

"I have a question, Dr. Brown."

"What is your question, Peddiwell?"

"Why doesn't the rule tell us how to identify those some-times?"

"That, Mr. Peddiwell, is a pertinent inquiry." (When the old gentleman mistered a boy, he was being complimentary. He complimented the girls, whom he always called *Miss*, by including the first name with the surname.) "The rule does not give us the desired information for the reason that there is no logical way of stating it. Latin is not always logical. It was made by human beings, illogical human beings. So there are many things about it we just have to know, bit by bit. But who wants to be logical all of the time or even most of the time?

> ....Great God! I'd rather be
> A Pagan suckled in a creed outworn,
> So might I, standing on this pleasant lea,
> Have glimpses that would make me less forlorn;
> Have sight of Proteus rising from the sea;
> Or hear old Triton blow his wreathed horn."

When I say that Dr. Brown taught us manners, I do not mean *etiquette* but rather *mores* in the classical sense. Consider his remark to an eight o'clock Greek class the morning after Mr. Ching Lee's encounter with One-Eyed Gibson.

Lee was the Chinese laundryman in the village where the academy was located. Everyone knew him. He was an industrious, courteous, and honorable citizen. He never had trouble with anybody except One-Eyed Gibson.

A livery stable next door to Lee's laundry was a favorite *rendez-vous* of Gibson, a character generally regarded as a no-good bum and suspected of being a petty if not occasionally a major criminal. He was a big, tough man, still on the youthful side of forty, and possessed of a sense of humor which required someone other than himself to get hurt. He liked alcoholic beverages, and their consumption deepened his sense of humor.

One evening, while celebrating some festive occasion with other *bon vivants* in the livery stable, Gibson, who had bothered

the laundryman before in other ways laughable to almost all on-
lookers but not very funny to Lee, figured out a new and funnier
joke. He turned the fire hose on Lee's baskets of freshly ironed
laundry, breaking a rear window to get the joke going. This was
Thursday night and Lee had been ironing steadily for two full
days. Early Friday morning, thinking of the irate housewives
who would soon be arriving for their laundry and dreading to
give them the news that it would take him three more days to re-
wash and re-iron the lot, the laundryman called on the county
sheriff and laid his problem before that officer. The sheriff's advice was eminently sensible and Western to the core. "He busted
into yore back room there illegally. Whyn't you take a God-
damn' gun to him?"

"No got gun," said Mr. Lee.

"Hah?" ejaculated the sheriff, astonished that any resident
of Oregon in the year 1908 should be weaponless. "I'll give you a
gun," he said, and then he picked a fair-looking Colt .44-40 from
his collection of confiscated weapons.

Lee took the gift politely but explained further, "Allee same
never fired gun. How you do?"

The sheriff's heart was really touched by this admission. He
took Lee out to the garbage dump and showed him how to shoot
rats.

Of course everybody in the community knew these details.
About a week later, One-Eyed Gibson returned from a "business
trip" from somewhere to somewhere and was immediately briefed
by his retainers. That night, or rather about two o'clock the next
morning, after a convivial session (not in the livery stable whose
owner because of unfavorable publicity had denied the use of his
premises to the Gibson gang, but in his own private quarters),
Gibson brought a bottle over to the laundry to seal a new era of
friendship with the Chinese.

"Come out here, you slant-eyed bastard," the would-be peace-
maker bawled, beating on Lee's front door, "an' have a drink
with me."

"No drink," said Lee. "Go 'way."

"Come out and have a drink," insisted Gibson, beginning to feel insulted. "You ain't too God-damn' good to drink with me."

"Go 'way from door or I shoot," said Lee.

"Why you yellow son of a bitch," shouted Gibson, now really enraged. "Open up that door and have a drink with me or I'll kick the God-damn' thing down, an' then I'll . . ."

He was already kicking on the door but he never finished his complete threat, for at this moment Lee fired twice through the upper panel. The first bullet hit Gibson in the neck and almost decapitated him. The second slug caught him in the chest as he was going down. As the sheriff said at the coroner's inquest, "Lee never shot Gibson but once. The second bullet went into a corpse."

All of us academy pupils had heard the news at breakfast. When the Greek class was assembled and the eight o'clock bell had rung, Dr. Brown said, "Before continuing to read Xenophon's account of the retreat of the ten thousand, let us pause to pay tribute to Mr. Ching Lee, a gentleman whom we all know and respect. At two o'clock this morning he rid our community of a worthless scoundrel and probably saved the State of Oregon the later cost of a hanging. Kindly begin translating at the top of page 42, Miss Bishop."

The curriculum that I followed at Dr. Brown's academy was somewhat unusual, even in that day. There were two curricula in the school; the classical one and the modern one. The difference resided in the languages studied. In the classical curriculum you had Latin, Greek, and one modern language, which meant French or German. In the modern curriculum, you had Latin and two modern languages, or you were even allowed to elect a course in European History in lieu of one of the language years.

There was no election for me. I studied what Dr. Brown told me to study. In the languages, this was four years of Latin, two years of Greek, two years of French, and eight years of English. The English was divided into four years of literature and four years of composition. The composition, in turn was divided into three hours a week of written exercises called rhetoric and two hours of oral composition variously called in the four years, public speaking, argumentation and debate, dramatic interpretation, and oratory.

In mathematics I had algebra the first year, plane geometry the second, intermediate algebra and solid geometry the third, and advanced algebra and trigonometry the fourth.

The four years of natural sciences began with physical geography in the first year, one semester each of physiology and botany in the second year, physics in the third year and in the fourth year one semester of geology and one of descriptive astronomy.

I attended classes six hours a day, five days a week. Since the regular classes ran from eight o'clock in the morning until five in the afternoon, I had one hour for lunch and two hours for study during the day. I picked up about three hours more study from seven to ten in the evening and occasionally an hour in the morning from six to seven. The modern observer will note at once that I had no instruction in the academy in history or other social studies. I forgot to mention, however, that we took one hour of the week for study of the Bible. In the first two years, the Old Testament was covered, the third year dealt with the Gospels, and the fourth year with the Epistles and Revelations.

We had no classes in art, music, or physical education. All such activities were extra-curricular. The sports were organized by the boys themselves. Such coaching as we received was a free service of some graduate or other citizen. I remember only one member of the teaching staff who ever did any coaching. That was the principal himself; he coached tennis. Our boxing coach was a local cigar store proprietor. He had been a bantamweight in his youth, and judging by the size and shapes of his ears he had not been very clever at defense. He was a good instructor, however.

Other activities were organized mainly by the so-called literary societies of which there were four, two each for boys and girls. Since the total enrollment of the academy was about 150, each society had a membership of 35 to 40. Membership in these societies was customary but not required. I can recall only one boy in my time who did not belong to a society. He regarded their activities as a waste of time. Life to him was too real and earnest to spend on such matters. He was an intensely religious boy, and I assumed that he spent the time saved by non-membership in prayer and meditation. I wish I could say that he became a famous clergyman, but the last I heard of him he was a traveling salesman for a salmon-packing outfit.

The society to which I belonged was the more agnostic of the boys' groups. We never went to the mid-week prayer meetings, for example. The compulsory daily chapel attendance at 7:30 A.M. seemed to us enough for reasonably close touch with the Deity.

Our society met every Thursday evening for two and one-half hours. Every member had some part in each meeting, were it only to answer the roll-call. The nature of the roll-call answer was announced one week in advance. One week it might be a one-minute comment on current state politics. The next week it could be a one-sentence boost of a national presidential candidate. The third week it might be a line of lyric poetry or an oratorical sentence.

The programs were usually supplied entirely by the members themselves. In four years attendance I do not recall any outside speakers. When old members, that is, graduates of the academy, attended a meeting, they were introduced, usually floridly, by a current member. They never made speeches in reply but only bowed their acknowledgement of applause. Sometimes they might be asked to be a judge or critic of the debate of the evening.

Programs were planned and places on them were assigned by the program committee about a month in advance. Approximately half the programs were debates. In my time they dealt almost exclusively with political, social, and economic questions. Most of the remaining programs were original dramatic sketches, orations, "dialogues," or other forms of public speaking. A member would be involved in one of these programs as a principal participant at least once a month and as a subordinate once or twice a month. When we had a debate, for example, there were three debaters on each side, three judges, a moderator, and a critic. Once a year the society had a joint program with that one of the girls' societies with which it had traditionally the more friendly relations. This was usually a play or an operetta. Once a year also the society had a formal dinner to which each member invited as many guests as he desired and could feed at the high banquet price of seventy-five cents per plate. The program at this dinner was mostly musical, a small orchestra, various quartets and duets, and some instrumental and vocal solos. The toastmaster and the two or three speakers observed rigorous time limits which, I believe, never exceeded ten minutes.

My society taught its members to speak within prescribed limits. If a speaker failed to observe the limit, he was stopped abruptly by the presiding officer and was assigned a punishment, usually the fatigue detail of sweeping the society's room for the next meeting.

Most of the instruction of the academy was of poor quality, but some of it, like that of Dr. Brown himself, was very good. I never happened to have a teacher of mathematics, for example (and I suppose I had at least a half-dozen in that field), who seemed to know anything about teaching any subject, and most of them appeared to be frightened by mathematics.

Of all the science courses I took, I recall only two that were taught by teachers who impressed me enough to have me remember their names for more than fifty years. One was the last science teacher I had in the academy, Professor Lyman Masters, who gave the course in descriptive astronomy. He opened every session of that course with a quotation of astronomical flavor from the Bible. Of course we all knew, "The heavens declare the glory of God and the firmament showeth his handiwork. Day unto day uttereth speech and night unto night showeth knowledge. There is no speech nor language where their voice cannot be heard." Masters knew scores of such verses. He must have acquired them by concordance study over a long period.

Curiously enough, after that first quotation each day, the professor never again referred to religion. He might start a session with a solemn reference to the morning star dancing for joy and then add without a pause, "We do not know the exact speed of light. Professor Michelson's recent measurements have pushed the limits of our ignorance back a trifle, but this is a problem that will require lifetimes of research."

I was Masters' pupil for the spring semester in 1909. Most of what he taught me, of course, I soon forgot, and much of it would now be wrong if I remembered it. Nevertheless I have a deep and persistent interest in astronomy that Masters gave me in that short period of instruction long ago. I read today in the field of astronomy everything I can understand and a considerable amount that I cannot understand. Masters put some kind of a *wakan* on me. I do not think the Biblical quotations had anything to do with it. They constituted a mere idiosyncrasy of a powerful teaching personality. I think he would have put the same *wakan* on me if his personal idiosyncrasy had been a glass of beer instead of a Biblical quotation at the beginning of each session of the astronomy class.

The other science teacher, whose name I remember but will not perpetuate in this account, was a pallid youth assigned to the teaching of physical geography, a kind of a general-science course that included some astronomical notions. I remember this teacher primarily for his lecture on the planetary hypothesis. He did not refer to its hypothetical character but spoke of it as though it were a law. The sun, he explained, was rotating like a big top. It was spinning counter-clockwise, as observed from its north pole. It threw off big hunks of molten material which settled into orbits and thus became the planets. "How did they rotate?" he asked impressively.

"Counter-clockwise," said a bright girl in the front row.

"That is correct," said the teacher. "They had to spin the same way as their parent sun."

All the front row nodded understandingly.

"But," continued the teacher, overjoyed at the bombshell he was about to throw, "some of our planets don't rotate counter-clockwise. They spin clockwise. How could that happen?"

Little Johnny Powers, the youngest member of the class, held up his hand. He thought the teacher was asking a real question. The teacher thought that he was asking a rhetorical one in preparation for his peroration. He scowled at Johnny. "Yes?" he snapped.

"Well—uh—" stammered Johnny eagerly, "those planets that now go the other way could have got tipped over as they were thrown off the sun, and so—uh—when you think you are looking down at their north poles you're really looking at their original south poles, and what is clockwise now was counterclockwise then."

The teacher was furious. "Where'd you read that?" he demanded.

"I—I didn't read it, sir," said Johnny.

"Hah! Of course you read it, or somebody must have told you. Don't try to make me believe that you are bright enough to have figured that out all by yourself. Who told you?"

Poor Johnny, who would not reach his twelfth birthday until the next summer, always shy, and small even for his age, was by this time practically speechless.

"Well—uh—you told us, sir, just now that . . ."

"Don't argue with me, you young smart-alec, or I'll make you regret the day you ever entered my class."

There was more of this, but even after more than a half-century it is painful for me to recall it.

SEVEN

Some Vocational Training

IN THE SPRING of 1909, at the age of sixteen, I was graduated from the Tum-a-Lum Academy. Jim, back in St. Paul, Minnesota, had just completed his first year in a public high school. Some of my decisions not to go to college the next year may have come from my desire to attend with Jim, although I am not sure of this. Perhaps I was entirely motivated by the normal impulse of a sixteen-year-old to take a place in the world of working men. I do not remember that Mr. Webster discussed the question with me. Work experience and work skills were highly prized by most young people whom I knew. I will not say that they were more highly prized than they are now, but certainly they were differently valued. We were closer to the frontier, and a variety of skills was more often of immediate use to a young man.

The fact that I was J. J. Webster's son kept me from seeking work in the cattle country. It would have been embarrassing for me to hold a horse-wrangling job, yet that was the kind of work in which I already had some skill. I could do the usual wrangler's chores, but I was sensitive about the kind of speculation that I knew would go on in the bunkhouses if I worked anywhere except on the Jay-Jay or Bar-W ranches.

Thus it happened that I drifted away from the cattle country into the timbered areas on the Pacific slope of the Coast Range, walking and carrying my bedroll. The year, 1909, with the West still feeling the after effects of the financial "panic" of 1907, was not propitious for casual labor. I first tried two logging camps and then a timber cruiser's small outfit. I was fed hospitably in each case but not given employment. Finally I heard of a road gang that might take on a man or two. It was working on the Wilson River about forty miles from where I received the news. I went to the place indicated, and on the evening of the second day of my journey I halted fairly close to the road camp. I preferred to make my request for employment at the start of a working day.

As I walked up to the camp the next morning, the gang was organizing for the day's work. A couple of teams of scrawny horses were being hitched to Fresno scrapers, but apparently most of the earth and rock moving was being done by pick and shovel with an occasional assist from a stick or two of dynamite. There were about a dozen men in the crew. I asked for the foreman, a cattle-country term, which I learned later sounded alien and "educated" to these timber-country homesteaders. They used the term *boss*. They indicated a rangy-looking, red-faced man about fifty years old. He stood by the side of the road, apparently observing the preparation for work with a mild interest. I approached him with my request.

"I heard maybe you could use a man," I said.

He looked at me appraisingly. "A *man*, yes," he said. "Let's see your hands."

A foreboding coolness crept up my spine, but I complied, thrusting my soft palms out for inspection. They were un-calloused. They had hardly touched a rope in ten months, much less a pick or shovel. The foreman glanced at them and turned a wad of cut plug in his cheek.

"A *man*, yes," he repeated, "but not a ribbon clerk."

I realized what I had to do, or rather what I thought I had to do, and I did not like it. It seemed to me, however, that if I were going to get any kind of job or have any kind of respectable personal status in these mountains, I would have to declare myself. I was a welterweight. In fact I had been the welterweight boxing champion of the Tum-a-Lum Academy, but I knew quite well that the academy was not a very big place. The foreman, I judged, was at least a light heavyweight. All this cogitation was swift, and my decision was automatic.

"It's your privilege, Mister, to turn me down for a job," I said as coolly as I could, "but if you'll take off that mackinaw jacket and step out into this little clearing, and if one of those yahoos knows enough to act as referee, I'll show you which one of us is a ribbon clerk."

The tall foreman made no motion toward removing his jacket, but all activity in the road gang halted abruptly. No prospective fighters ever had a more attentive audience.

"Marquis of Queensberry rules, I suppose," said the foreman reflectively.

"Right," I said and then added, "I'd like that nearest teamster there to serve as my second, if he'll be so kind." I had caught a gleam in the man's eye that pleased me. This and the fact that he was driving horses gave me the basis of choice.

"Well," said the foreman judicially, "I don't know that you'll be needing a second, because I don't think there'll be a fight. I don't believe I want to fight. You gave the challenge. I refuse it. I guess I made a mistake about you being a ribbon clerk. I guess maybe you're a prize fighter, and I don't want to get my ears beat down."

"No sir, I'm not a fighter," I assured the foreman swiftly. I was abashed and emotionally let down by the quick turn of events.

"Well, anyway," he said serenely, "I guess I can use you after all. Grab a shovel there. And here," he added drawing a pair of canvas work-gloves from his jacket pocket. "I'll loan you these to pertect your lily-white hands."

This was my introduction to Matt (for Matthew) Higby, and I am still ashamed of it. After I got acquainted with him I realized that if we had fought he would probably have whipped me in one round. If I had merely protested that I was not a ribbon clerk and that I was willing to be tried out, I could have had a job without the absurd, youthful heroics. But Matt understood men, particularly young men. He knew what motivated them, and he had a vast sympathy for them.

"Gosh," said Bill Reigner, the teamster, as he showed me where I could make a bed next to his in the bunk tent that evening. "You're the first boy I ever heard challenge the old man. Would you of actually fought him?"

"I guess I would have had to," I said, "or my second would have been mighty ashamed of me."

"By Golly, I *would* have served as your second," said Bill earnestly. "You didn't know nobody; somebody *had* to be your second."

"I sure appreciate it, Bill," I said, and he beamed at me. I was already captivated by his mild blue eyes, his freckles, and his sure judgments concerning the right thing to do.

I worked with Matt's gang until the road-building season ended in September. I did not acquire many new manual skills. Occasionally when a tree had to be removed from the trail, I profited by helping those timber-wise laborers fall and cut it up. My most important learning in this period, however, was not a skill. It was rather an attitude of appreciation which I gained mainly from Bill Reigner and Matt Higby.

Later, both in the Army and in civilian life, I was to meet and work with other men like Bill. All too rarely I was to see men as able as Matt leading them. I understood them better because I had been in Matt's road gang in the summer of 1909.

Bill was a man whose intelligence level put him barely into the normal group, yet his social qualities were exceptionally high. It was hard for him to solve any sort of intellectual problem, but he had a remarkable capacity for making correct moral choices.

Such men have to be led, although in small circles they are often leaders themselves. They distrust leadership that begins by emphasizing an intellectual issue. One who aspires to lead them must capture their loyalty by setting up a standard of values around which they can rally. That standard has to be stated inductively in terms of individuals. These men comprehend such a standard all the more readily because that is the way they have to operate their own personal affairs. They lack the capacity to make a reasoned, generalized approach to problems. They have to rely on specific moral benchmarks.

You didn't know nobody; somebody had to be your second.

I got my next job with ease through the kind offices of Matt Higby. He recommended me to Peter McNerney, foreman of a railroad construction gang in the Willamette Valley, by a letter which I remember word for word. He showed it to me after he had written it with a stubby pencil on a cigarette paper. It read:

Dear Pete—
　　This boy is a good worker.
　　　　　　　Respectfully,
　　　　　　　Matt Higby

At first I did general labor on McNerney's gang, carrying ties and helping lay rails, but after a few weeks I was promoted to the slightly more skilled job of driving spikes. I suppose I had a somewhat faster reaction time than the average laborer, and I soon developed the knack of hitting the spike squarely with maximum force. Thus I became a hammer man. My chief memory of the three months during which I worked on this job is one of pride in that skill. I had begun to acquire the first characteristic of a professional in any field, a concern for techniques. Anybody of ordinary strength could drive spikes; the professional hammer man was one who could drive them more elegantly than the ordinary man. To be a professional, one had first of all to be conscious of the need for that elegance.

The railroad construction job was completed early in December. I was again looking for work, and now I found that jobs were very hard to find. I tramped about the Willamette Valley, occasionally riding on freight trains when I happened to spot a brakeman who remembered my having worked for McNerney, but all leads proved false. Men were being laid off rather than hired. I was almost ready to apply as a last resort for a job on one of the dairy farms that dotted the Valley, although I shuddered at the thought of having to learn to milk cows. In the cattle country we generally used condensed milk extracted from cans. Once in a while, to get fresh milk in an emergency for babies or invalids, we milked beef cows by tying them to a fence and having a calf suckle them from one side while we sneaked a cupful or two of milk from the other side. This activity was called calf-robbing. It was generally regarded with scorn even by the poor devils who sometimes had to do it.

I finally landed a job almost by accident. I say *almost* because it was not an accident that led me to walk up a side road that morning. It was the sound of a heavy hammer striking steel. If I had not regarded myself as a kind of hammer man, I might not have followed that sound. I might have walked on to the next farm and applied for work. The farmer might have given me a job. Thus I might have come at last to the actual degradation of being a calf-robber. The pastures thereabouts were filled with Holsteins, Jerseys, and Guernseys. Their aristocratic and self-satisfied airs both irritated and fascinated me. I knew that I was about ready to become one of their valets.

The sound of that hammer saved me from ever having a closer acquaintance with dairy cows than that gained by looking at them over a page-wire fence. It led me to a rock quarry where about a dozen men were working. Four or five of them were loading a wagon with heavy blocks of stone. They had a big tripod arrangement with a block-and-tackle attachment to manhandle these chunks of rock. A few other men were shoveling gravel into wheelbarrows and trundling it over to a chute which led down to another wagon on a lower level of the quarry.

I took in this much detail with a glance and then watched intently the two men in whose work I was really interested. One of them sat on a rock holding a steel drill which the other man struck with a sledge hammer. I think I had never seen a rock quarry before except at a distance from a train or a wagon road. I am sure that I had never seen anyone striking drill before. I did not realize that there should be two men striking and that the crew was therefore short one hammer man. I supposed that the drill-holder and the striker spelled one another from time to time.

I sensed at once that these two men belonged in the upper ranks of labor in the rock quarry. They were obviously doing a job that called for polished precision. I had no idea when I descended into the quarry that I would apply for anything other than a laboring job on the lowest echelon.

The men who were loading rocks onto the wagon indicated that the boss was the man holding the drill. I walked over to him and waited for a lull in the striking. The hammer man immediately stopped. Actually he needed a rest, as I could well understand later, for he was trying to do two men's work. He pulled a red bandana from his hip pocket and wiped the sweat from his face. It was a frosty morning, but he must have been swinging that eight-pound hammer considerably faster than usual. He was trying, of course, to keep up with the drill-holder who had nothing to do between blows but to keep the drill straight and give it a quarter of a turn.

"Sure glad to see you," said the striker. "Old Slave-Driver Van here is a twistin' that there drill faster'n ordinary. He wants to make a record. He wants to see how long I can go before I drop stone-cold dead of heart failure."

The drill-holder removed a corncob pipe with a very short stem from his teeth. "Ah, hell," he said grinning. "You ain't hardly warmed up yet." Then to me, he remarked, "Howdy, nice mornin'."

I applied for work with no real notion of getting any. To me there seemed to be plenty of men on hand for the job in operation. The foreman assumed, I suppose, that I knew enough about rock quarries to see at a glance that he was short a drill-striker.

"You a hammer man?" he asked.

I was surprised but proud to be able to say that I was a kind of hammer man. I said that I had driven spikes on the railroad but that I had never struck drill.

"Heft that hammer," he said. I took the tool the striker

handed me. "Is it like the ones you used on the railroad?" he asked.

I swung the hammer tentatively. "It's about the same weight," I said, "but this one has a little longer handle and seems to be better balanced in some way."

I made this judgment in honest innocence, but nothing else that I could have said would have introduced me more favorably to the drill-striker. I think he regarded me as a fellow professional from that point forward.

"Heh, heh!" he chortled. "That ain't no doggone railroad spike maul. That's a real hammer."

"I need a striker, as you can see," said the foreman. "I lost a good one yesterday. He had to go back to Colorado to help his dad work a coal mine. You left- or right-handed?"

He was not asking about my handedness in general but about my preference in using a two-handed hammer. I was glad to report that I was ambidextrous. On the railroad I had driven spikes either way.

"That's good," said the foreman. "Webb, here, can hit from both sides, but it's easier for him to strike right-handed." Then to Webb he said, "Get him a hammer from the tool shed."

I wanted a job, but while Webb was gone for the hammer I raised the question of whether my experience was good enough for this job. Although I did not mention my concern for the drill-holder's hands, that was what I was thinking of. Those railroad spikes I had struck so confidently had nobody holding them.

The foreman was mildly surprised. "Oh, sure, you can do it," he said persuasively. "Just take it easy and always remember to keep your eye on the head of the drill."

For the first hour, I was definitely ill at ease. I struck each blow with infinite care, although Webb and I were hitting almost as fast as a regular team. When we got the first hole drilled and were moving over to a new position, both the boss and my fellow striker were complimentary.

"You doin' plum all right," said Webb.

"Sure he is," said Van. "He's an old hammer man from Hammertown. You can see that."

Under the relaxing influence of this flattery, I struck a little faster until Webb and I were keeping abreast of the drill-holder. That is to say, we were striking as fast as Van could clear his steel and move it the quarter turn after each blow. I was still swinging each time, however, with utmost care, conscious of the damage I could inflict on the drill-holder's hands if I missed that steel just once.

At noon I was confronted by an embarrassing situation. I had no lunch. The other men, living in the village five miles away, where I had stayed the night before, or on neighboring farms, carried their lunches to the quarry in buckets and paper sacks. Webb and Van both offered me major shares of their lunches, but knowing how hungry they must be I accepted only a sandwich from one and an apple from the other. I pled in explanation that I had eaten an unusually heavy breakfast. That was a mistake on my part. By two o'clock in the afternoon, I was wishing that I had accepted at least one more sandwich.

About three o'clock I began to get really weary. Striking drill is rather harder work than driving spikes on the railroad. When you drive a spike, you tap it lightly to get it started, you hit it one or two good licks, and it is finished. Then you step over to drive the next one. When you strike drill, there is none of this tapping and stepping-over routine. You just stand there in your tracks, part of a delicately timed three-man enterprise; you swing, you strike, you swing, you strike, and you keep this up for quite a period—sometimes, indeed, for an eternity—before you can relax. This is a job that requires endurance—and elegance. I speak as a hammer man from Hammertown itself.

I am afraid I am trying to postpone the evil tale I have to tell. Part of the fatigue I felt that afternoon was physical, probably more of it was nervous exhaustion. I was still striking each blow with care, and that care was wearing on me.

I have already mentioned Van's short-stemmed pipe. He did not smoke it a great deal. It went out easily, as pipes do, and then he could not fire it up again until we had finished a hole. He kept it in his mouth much of the time, nevertheless. Occasionally the drill stuck a little, and Van would lean forward in an effort to jerk it loose and get it turned before the next hammer blow fell. When he leaned forward in this fashion, his pipe would sometimes come rather near the path of the hammer.

Van had told me to keep my eye on the head of the drill, and I knew personally that I had to watch the drill in order to hit it. This is an example of something learned verbally and fully accepted by the learner but still requiring a more complete learning. The word had to be made flesh to me in that connection.

I fell to glancing at that pipe whenever Van jerked on the steel. I was now on the danger line. I was attending to too many things. After looking at the pipe I would immediately look back at the drill head, but the process helped sap my nervous energy. Suddenly I looked from the pipe to the steel just as I started a downward swing. I sensed in horror that I was going to miss the head of the drill. I tried to stop my blow, pulling back on the hammer desperately. By so doing, I may have hit Van's leg less sharply than I might otherwise have done. There is also the possibility that if I had not pulled back on the hammer I might have hit the drill after all. Maybe the sudden conviction that I was going to miss was merely an illusion in the first place.

But I did miss and there sat Van with the right leg of his overalls torn from just below the knee to his ankle, and a raw, red welt showing on his leg through the slashed cloth.

I stood trembling. I was not concerned about the job I thought I was losing but about the way in which I was losing it. I was aghast as a hammer man that I had missed a blow and hurt the drill-holder. I do not remember my stammered apologies, but I am sure that they were profuse and incoherent.

"That's all right," said Van carelessly. "Go ahead."

Then I realized that he expected me to continue striking.

"But I hit you!" I cried. "I tore your pants and cut your leg!"

He looked down at his injury as though noticing it for the

first time. "Ah, hell," he said. "Them pants was about wore out anyway, and that little scratch on my leg don't amount to naw-thin'. Keep a hittin'." Then, as he saw my continued hesitation, he looked directly at me for the first time since I had struck him.

"Every man," he said calmly, "is entitled to miss the drill once in a while."

I stared back at that round-faced philosopher for a moment, and suddenly I felt an iron band removed from my chest.

"All right," I said, and I swung the hammer back. Van set the drill as the hammer came up. I swung down with full power. Van made the turn, and then Webb's hammer followed. Again I struck and, watching the drill carefully, I knew that I would not miss it again. I struck drill for Willem Van Ek from December 10, 1909 to June 30, 1911, and I never did miss the drill again.

Van Ek, I believe, was never a soldier or a student in any educational institution more advanced than a one-room rural school, but for a half-century he was the guardian angel for every soldier and every student who came before a court of inquiry or a disciplinary committee of which J. Abner Peddiwell was a member.

EIGHT

The Danebod School

IN THE SUMMER of 1911, Mr. Webster, Jim and I took a vacation. It was a canoe-fishing trip for two months in the lake country on the Minnesota-Manitoba border. We had two canoes and a guide for the expedition. Since either Jim or I always traveled in the canoe with the guide, Mr. Webster had one of his sons with him each day.

One day, when Mr. Webster and I were traveling together, he asked me whether I was going to start college work that fall. I replied that since Jim had only another year to complete high school I had thought of working one more year and entering college with him. Mr. Webster then asked me what I planned to work at. I said I might get a hammer job somewhere. He seemed to understand my pride in being a good hammer man, but he was not greatly impressed by it. He asked me whether I had thought of being a teacher, and he knew in detail the requirements of the time for a rural teacher's certificate in Minnesota, Montana, and Oregon.

"If you were my age and had only secondary education, would you try to teach school," I asked, "or would you start to build up a big ranching business?"

He laughed shortly. "There's no question about that," he said. "I would sure like to have been a teacher if I had ever had the qualifications on even the most beginning level. But we're not talking about my life. I've lived most of it already. We're talking about yours. You've got that quarter section your father home-steaded on Juniper Creek and that adjoining half-section I bought up for you with the money you've been sending me from your wages. You could start a ranch right now with those 480 acres."

This, as nearly as I can remember, was my vocational guidance into teaching. There were two circumstances which blocked my becoming a small rancher; I had too much scholastic education and I had the wrong foster father. If I became a rancher, I would have to try to become a big one, and I doubted that I was a second J. J. Webster.

I got my first teaching position strictly through my own efforts and an impressive letter to a Southwestern Minnesota county school superintendent from Henry Liberty Brown, Ph.D., D.D., LL.D. Dr. Brown attested to my having completed the classical curriculum of the Tum-a-Lum Academy in a satisfactory and honorable manner. The first of those adjectives no doubt referred to my scholastic attainments and the second to the fact that the sheriff had no warrant out for me. Dr. Brown also appended a detailed listing of all the subjects I had studied. He added, in a cryptically complimentary manner, that I was a young man "of serious purpose who will go to great lengths to complete whatever he undertakes." I know these details because the county school superintendent insisted on reading them to me.

For two days I studied various books and pamphlets in the superintendent's office. Then I took a special county teachers' examination on the common branches and in teaching theory and practice. I passed the examination with a score of 100 in grammar, orthography, arithmetic, and physiology. In history, geography, civics, and theory and practice of teaching, my scores ranged from 95 to 80. In penmanship I received the minimum passing grade of 65 and a warning from the superintendent that I must make heroic efforts to improve in that subject if I wanted to get anywhere in the teaching profession. I took the warning seriously. I tried for years to raise my level of penmanship. As a result, I can testify that I could write a better hand in September, 1911, than I have ever been able to write since that date.

The superintendent commended me by letter to the attention of the Danebod school board where they still lacked a teacher for the coming year. I rented a mount from a livery stable and rode out to Danebod, twenty-seven miles away, with the letter in hand. I arrived in the afternoon, stayed that night in the house of the chairman of the board, and had my official interview with the board at seven o'clock the next evening.

After questioning me about my command of the "common branches," ability to "control the scholars," and knowledge of school law, the board excused me and went into executive session. I returned to the house of the chairman, Soren Jensen, to await the board's decision. Within a half-hour he came home and announced my election.

I asked Jensen for advice concerning a place to board. He called his wife into consultation. She recommended a place which I found eminently satisfactory.

Mrs. Jensen's linguistic gifts were remarkable. She had come to the United States twelve years earlier without knowing a word of English and with only elementary schooling in Denmark. She had been a housewife on a homestead for those twelve years with limited opportunities for conversation with anyone except her husband and children. Yet now she could read and write English entirely adequately, and in addition she had what must have been one of the world's greatest abilities to speak extemporaneously, exhaustively, and effectively on any subject within the range of her interest. I heard her speak in her native tongue on later occasions. She appeared to be as fluent in Dano-Norse as in English. It seemed to me that she could not possibly be more fluent in any tongue than in English.

I asked her one time how she had managed to learn English so well when her husband was working on his farm and her children were too small to talk. "I read in the newspaper and in books from the school," she said, "and then I talked to myself about what I had read."

I had about ten days left before the beginning of the school term. First I looked the school building over very carefully and checked its furniture and equipment against the *State Requirements for a Standard Rural School*. We had a dictionary, a good coal-burning stove with a sheet-iron jacket designed to distribute the heat uniformly throughout the room. We had a separate shed, a lean-to arrangement on the back end of the school lot. The only things missing were a flag and a flagpole. I was commissioned to buy the flag in the county seat, and Mr. Jensen committed himself to furnishing a flagpole from his windbreak where a straight, twenty-foot pine was available for cutting.

I rode the livery-stable horse back to the county seat after being at Danebod three days. I spent two more days reading in the county superintendent's office. I also bought a horse, an eight-year-old bay gelding, for twenty dollars. I got him cheap because he was a little hard to handle. I received also the loan of a saddle and bridle with him until I could have my own rig expressed to me from Oregon. I called this horse *Mr. Sperry* for a reason which now escapes me. Perhaps it was because he circled a great deal as he was being mounted until I had given him some schooling.

It is probably unnecessary to report that when I rode back to Danebod I contracted with the widow, Mrs. Gjerda Hansen, for my board at ten dollars per month, washing included. She set this figure herself. She had also been briefed by Mrs. Jensen without doubt. I arranged with Sigurd Larsen, Mrs. Hansen's father, moreover, for the board of my horse at two dollars a month.

After detailing these minor financial items, I should add the major information that my salary at Danebod was fifty dollars per month. The school month was precisely four weeks, or twenty school days. Thus I was paid $2.50 per working day. My salary was about ten dollars per month higher than the average rural teacher's salary for that county. Part of this was given to me for not being a woman, but a considerable portion of it was a recognition of my advanced schooling, particularly that Greek which gave me such uniqueness.

The Danebod schoolhouse was a 24 by 40-foot structure set

on a knoll of about two acres. It and its flanking outhouses were painted a dull, almost rusty, barn red. There was no tree or even a small shrub of any kind on the school grounds. Apparently the plot had been chosen because of its complete unsuitability for agricultural purposes. Its surface made a hazardous playground because it was mostly coarse gravel. However, snow came early that year and made the school ground beautiful.

The school furniture included a teacher's desk and chair and fifteen double-desk-and-seat combinations. The desks were arranged in three rows of five each. One row was for primary children, a second for children of intermediate size, and a third for children who were as large as adults. Coats and headgear were hung on hooks to the right and left of the entrance door. A water bucket and basin stood on a bench near the entrance. Back of the teacher's desk was a three-shelved bookcase, and to one side of it was a blackboard on an easel. On the other side was a cottage organ.

All these physical details are unimportant, however. The important circumstance about Danebod to me was that this was the most civilized community in which I had ever lived. It was civilized because it was peopled almost exclusively by immigrants from the most civilized country of Western Europe. All the children in the school were Danish born or of Danish descent on both sides of the family, except the Nelson children. They were only fifty per cent Danish; their father had been born in Norway.

Men and women of this community who were between thirty and sixty years old in 1911 had been brought up in the period of the later nineteenth-century Danish cultural and economic renaissance. In their educational and religious views, they were practically all followers of the doctrines of Nicolai F. S. Grundtvig, the Danish bishop, whose notions of the Living Word as being more important than "dead books" had been the mainspring of the Danish renaissance of 1870–1910. They believed in the Living Word, and they looked for it in all aspects of life.

There were twenty-seven pupils enrolled in the Danebod school at the beginning of the year. They were in the first to fourth and sixth to eighth grades inclusive. The fifth grade was missing because brilliant little Stella Jensen three years earlier had gone directly from the first into the third grade, and Sigurd Nelson's parents had moved to Minneapolis. Sigurd, said the children impressively, as though speaking of something extraordinary, was a full-blooded Norwegian but a first cousin of the current Nelsons in the school.

The Danebod teacher was not entirely ignorant of professional lore. The days of feverish reading of State-Department-of-Education manuals and pamphlets must be taken into account. I recall two other days of intensive preparation, moreover, about the middle of October, when the teachers' institute was held in the county seat. I think salaries were paid for attendance. I remember signing a card and presenting it to the usher as I entered each session.

We had general "inspirational" programs in the early morning and in the evening meetings. In the later forenoon and early afternoon sessions there were departmental meetings of various kinds; high-school English teachers, primary reading, rural-school registers, and the like. I believe I spent all my departmental time with a specialist in the teaching of penmanship. No doubt this reflected my feeling of inadequacy in that discipline.

The specialist in penmanship wore pince-nez eyeglasses attached to a wide black cord that could almost be called a ribbon. He wore a flowing black bow tie. He had rather long black hair brushed in studied negligence almost down to his collar. It is hardly necessary to add that his coat and trousers were shiny black. His boiled shirt and detachable cuffs, of course, were gleaming white. I learned from bemused attention to his words, when not distracted by his dramatic gestures, that no one could write well who failed to use his whole arm in the process. At least that is my memory of this instruction, although I may have misunderstood it. On careful examination of my memory, indeed, I am inclined to believe that I did misunderstand.

My only other clear memory of this teachers' institute is that of the main speaker's peroration at the final general session. He wept. I am not speaking metaphorically. He shed actual tears. I saw them coursing down his cheeks. I do not remember why he was weeping. I guess he was emotionally overcome by his own eloquence. He was quoting Tennyson's *Crossing the Bar*. I have never again been able to hear those lines, ... *a-and one c-clear c-call for m-me...*, without incipient laughter. I hope I did not laugh on that October evening.

Since 1911 I have myself given hundreds of inspirational speeches to teachers' institutes. They are now called pre-service workshops or other similarly modern names, but they are the same old institutes when I get up and turn on the oratory. I never quote Tennyson, however, and I never weep. To make the audience laugh or cry is permissible and often unavoidable. To laugh at one's own wit, however, is inelegant; and to weep at one's own pathos is unforgivable and should be punished by expulsion from SATIS (Society of American Teachers' Institute Speakers). The organization's motto, naturally, is *Satis, satis est*.

The really important and long-lasting professional education that I received during this school year, however, came from the urbane and intelligent pupils of the Danebod district. I taught four of them to read, for example, but they taught me that mutual trust and warm affection were super-technical instruments of great power in any learning situation.

Three of the beginners, Eddie Andersen and the Sorensen twins, Inger and Peter, were six years old. The fourth beginner, little Mary Nelson, was only five and one-half. She came first as a visitor, but she so enjoyed school and so desired to learn to read that I winked at the regulation which required her to have reached the age of six years. At the outset I carried her on my rolls as a kind of permanent visitor, but on November 12 when she reached the age of five years and seven months I said to myself, "She is nearer six than five years old," and registered her officially. She had taught me the First Principle of Administrative Parsimony which reads, *Any rule made by an administrator can be broken by an administrator when he feels like it and thinks he can get away with it.*

I taught the beginners to read by first having them learn to say their A-B-C's. Eddie already knew his letters, so I made him the A-B-C coach. Since Mary and Inger sat in the first primary seat and Eddie and Peter in the second, the four could study and recite to Eddie at will. The second morning they all knew how to say their letters. We then proceeded to learn to write our names and identify each letter in those words. Next we started reading in the primer, but we also made up little stories which we wrote on the blackboard in the morning before school or at noon-time and covered with an eraser-cloth, so that they would be a surprise. The only thing I can remember as being in the nature of a difficulty in teaching these four children to read was little Mary's shyness in reading aloud. She would sit on my lap and whisper the words in my ear, but she was too embarrassed by the large audience of three classmates to stand up and read right out loud.

Etta Rigby, my first assistant teacher, finally diagnosed the difficulty. "Mary can read out loud as well as any of those first-graders," explained Etta, "but she likes to sit on your lap." With this insight available, we soon had Mary reading in loud, clear tones and still sitting on my knee.

I see now that I will have to explain about my assistant teachers. Etta Rigby was two years older than I. She entered school that fall in the eighth grade, because in her earlier schooling she had completed only the seventh grade. She had been working in a millinery shop in Mankato for five years but had come home to Danebod on the death of her mother to take over the duties of keeping house for her father and her younger brother, twelve years old. Her father had persuaded her to go to school with her brother and get her eighth-grade certificate. Let me say right here that her decision to do so was a very fortunate event for me. Etta Rigby was one of the most charming and cultivated women I have ever known. Not long ago she was retired after forty years of distinguished service as a teacher of Latin and French in the high schools of Minnesota.

I am sure that it was Etta's influence, furthermore, that

brought me my second assistant teacher about November first. He was John E. Swenson, a twenty-four-year-old homesteader, who announced that he had never gone beyond the fourth grade and would probably have to start at that point. I had apparently been consulting more pamphlets, because at this juncture I began to be radical. I said that I would coach Etta and Johnny for the eighth-grade examinations by having them help me teach and particularly help me with the sixth, seventh, and eighth grades; and that to pay them for being my assistant teachers I was signing them up for University of Minnesota extension-division correspondence-study courses in first-year Latin, elementary algebra, and first-year English. I paid the small fees and bought the textbooks for these high-school courses myself. We went over the study outlines, the textbook assignments, and the questions for each lesson together. When did we do this? From 8:00 to 9:00 A.M., while we were eating lunch, and on our way to and from church. We also attended choir practice together, and we went to most of the dances given by the homesteaders within a radius of twenty miles. In fact we often played for the dances. John Swenson was a pretty good violinist, Etta could play a cottage organ very well, and I could play a guitar a little. During the year, Johnny taught me to play a few fiddle tunes, I taught Etta to chord on the guitar, and she taught me to play chords on the organ. Thus we could furnish the music for a dance and at the same time spell one another off for an occasional dance ourselves.

We had opening exercises in the school every morning for fifteen minutes. This period always included a group song, an individual recitation from some pupil, and a solo or duet accompanied on the organ by Etta or some one of her numerous cottage-organ pupils, or by Etta or me on the guitar. On Friday afternoons from 2:30 to 4:00 we always had a more formal program which included little plays that in those days for some obscure reason were called "dialogues," original recitations, and musical numbers that might feature a trio or a quartet.

I learned to build up my subordinates. Johnny or Etta took

turns in presiding over the morning exercises, and we had various pupil chairmen for the different features of the Friday afternoon programs.

Our physical-education activities were not neglected, but we were too uninformed to call them anything but games. Johnny and Etta led in all sorts of run-sheep-run, prisoner's-base, and ball games. I took part in those too but also spent whole hours at a time teaching wrestling. My boys, weight for weight, could throw any other boys in Southwestern Minnesota.

When the nearby lake froze solidly, the children cleared about ten acres for a real skating rink. Johnny and some of the seventh-and eighth-grade boys rigged up a pump to get water on top of the rough ice at night until they had the finest, smoothest skating surface I have ever seen.

I sharp-shod Mr. Sperry myself to make sure he would have secure footing and then I hauled all the sleds the school could muster out on the lake in tandem formation until the horse was at a full run. When I pulled him up to a polo turn and cracked the whip, the sleds swung in a crescendo of screaming laughter. Etta and Johnny were always on the last sled. They graded the children carefully as to their position on the sleds so that the smaller ones were nearest Mr. Sperry and were carefully held by responsible guardians. No child ever got hurt on those wild runs. That would really have been a miracle except with those miraculous Danes.

Those children never bullied one another. Any tendency in that direction was promptly nipped in the bud by the older children. All the older children stood *in loco parentis* to all the younger ones. They were civilized children from a civilized community. It was an inestimable privilege to have been permitted to begin teaching by teaching them.

In those days I knew nothing about mental ages or intelligence quotients. It is my considered opinion now that there was no child in the Danebod school who did not have at least superior intelligence. President Edward Holger Andersen of a certain state college in the Upper Mississippi Valley would undoubtedly disagree with me. One summer, about twenty-five years ago, when he was a young school superintendent, he took my graduate course in comparative education at Northern State University. There were more than one hundred students in that class, but I noted Andersen as being very tall, very intelligent, and very quiet. He wrote a brilliant term report, which my assistant brought particularly to my attention, and he passed the final examination with a superior score. I gave him a mark of *A* for the course.

A day or two after the summer quarter had ended, Andersen entered my office and asked, "Have you turned in your grades for Comparative Education yet?"

"Yes, I have," I assured him, somewhat astonished at the question from him. He did not seem to me to be the kind of student who would worry unduly about his grades. "You received . . . ," I began, but he interrupted me genially.

"I don't care what I got," he said. "I just wanted to be sure that you had turned in the grades before I told you who I was."

"I know who you are, Mr. Andersen," I said, mystified. "You are superintendent of schools at Talking Lake Junction."

"Heh, heh," he laughed. "I am Eddie Andersen of the first grade at Danebod. I was your A-B-C coach."

"Why, damn your eyes," I cried, grasping his hand. "Why didn't you tell me at the beginning of the quarter?"

"I know you like a book," he said. "You would have given me an *A* whether I deserved it or not. You thought all of us Danebod kids were geniuses."

"You *were* geniuses," I said.

He laughed again. "We were all ordinary dumb little Danes," he said, "but we worked as hard as we could to keep you from finding it out."

NINE

Culture and
Cordwood Sticks

JIM AND I entered the University of the West together in September, 1912. I was nineteen and he was seventeen years old. I suppose now that I must have selected the college we were going to enter, but I have no memory of our discussion of the matter, if any. The university was in Oregon and the Tum-a-Lum Academy was its preparatory school. That was probably the basis for my choice. It seems incredible that at the age of nineteen, with all the higher educational institutions of the country available to us, I should have made such a choice. To the young in heart, however, all cats are rather gray who claim to be gray.

No college with which I have ever been acquainted was more inappropriately named than the University of the West. In the first place, the institution was not in 1912, it had not been since its founding in 1846, and it has never been since 1912 a university. In 1912 it had a four-year curriculum of strictly undergraduate character taught by a singularly undistinguished faculty, most of whom did not know what a university was, and at least half of whom were not qualified to teach their subjects in secondary school.

In the second place, this college was as far from being an institution serving the whole West as could readily be imagined. It did not even serve any significant portion of the state in which it was located. Ninety per cent of its students came from an area within a radius of forty miles of its campus. When Jim and I came from the Jay-Jay Ranch, 120 miles from the college, we were about the most "foreign" of its students in terms of the distance traveled to register.

The founders of the University of the West must have been men of far-reaching, proud vision, but their hopes were dashed against the solid rocks of local reality. The school was designed to educate Christian ladies and gentlemen from all over the "Great West" for positions of leadership. Instead of playing that grand role, however, it gave a little post-secondary education to local young men and women who were no more Christian than their less well-schooled fellows.

The University had a pretty good football team in the fall of 1912, however, to shift to a topic often regarded as important in considering the history of any American higher educational institution. I was right tackle and Jim was right end. The guards and the center were good. The left tackle was very big but rather slow. He was a bulwark on defense. The left end was not as big as Jim but was fast and rugged. In the backfield we had plenty of beef and a modicum of brains. We did all right, winning somewhat more than our share of the games.

Try as hard as I can, however, I find myself unable at this date to recall anything of consequence I learned on the football field. I am aware of the sterling educational benefits accruing very generally to players of this game, but I am not aware that I received any of them. I was never hurt seriously in the game. I remember very little about the whole experience except my pride in Jim.

Jim weighed 175 pounds at that time and was just six feet tall. He looked like Mr. Webster, except for his high-bridged nose which was similar to that of his mother. He talked like Mr. Webster. He acted like Mr. Webster. He handled himself well and moved fast and precisely. Later at a state university which he attended from 1913 to 1916 he put on ten more pounds and became a very good player.

After the football season I entered the wrestling squad and also tried out for the debate team. I made both teams. Jim went out for the boxing team and was ranked third among the institution's light heavyweights, which I considered a good showing for a seventeen-year-old boy.

In the spring I went out for track, competing in the 220-yard dash and the three-mile cross-country run. Do not ask me how I came to specialize in two such varied events. I suppose that now I would not be permitted to do it, but then it seemed entirely proper. The 220 simply required a fast start and a burst of speed for some twenty-odd seconds. The three-mile run required second and third winds. I liked the dash better, but I was prouder to be able to do the three-mile run.

Jim did not go out for track. I regret to say also that the college had no baseball squad.

Turning now to our scholastic activities, I remember that we studied English composition, college algebra, chemistry, history of modern Europe, and Bible, which were apparently weighted in accord with their academic importance. The composition course met three hours a week, as did the history course. The algebra and chemistry courses were presumably sixty-six and two-thirds per cent more valuable for freshmen than the English composition and history, since they met the equivalent of five lecture hours per week. I say, "the equivalent," in a considered manner, for, although the algebra course did meet five hours per week, the chemistry course had two hours of lectures and six hours of laboratory work per week. The laboratory time had only fifty per cent as much scholarly magic as sitting in the lecture room. The course in Bible, given the primary purpose of the college, to educate Christian ladies and gentlemen, would appear to have needed at least ten hours a week; it was given only one hour. Perhaps these freshmen were assumed to have entered the institution already possessed of most of the requisite characteristics of Christian ladies and gentlemen. Perhaps a study of the Bible was really thought not to be very important in developing ... but I recoil from this thought and refuse to pursue it further.

Of the subjects studied in the freshman year, the only one I remember with any degree of vividness is the one that was taught only one hour per week, the Bible. The reason my memory singles out this discipline is not so much religious as personal. My class in Bible in the first semester, 1912–13, was taught by William Preston MacFarland.

MacFarland was a minister of the founding denomination of the university. Before entering upon theological training he had received his bachelor of arts degree *magna cum laude* from one of the most liberal of the Western liberal arts colleges. Before entering college he had been for two years a lumberjack in the Puget Sound region. He was a graduate of a famous divinity school attached to a great Eastern university, but fortunately for me, if not for himself, he had begun in 1911 to have doubts about the validity of his call to the ministry and had decided to shift to teaching to see whether his service in that vineyard might be received with more favor in the eyes of the Lord.

For some reason which I cannot now re-create, I got into MacFarland's class after it had been going for a week or two. I slid into a seat in the back row as the handsome young professor (he was then thirty-three years old) inquired, "Who owned these swine?"

A pallid youth in the front row, who was already known on the campus as a prospective minister of the gospel, answered earnestly, "The Bible says that they were Gadarene swine, so some Gadarene farmer must have owned them."

"And they were destroyed," said MacFarland thoughtfully.

The embryo preacher squirmed a little and said with pathetic precision, "The evil spirits that Jesus had driven from the poor man who had been possessed of them entered the swine and drove them into the sea."

"And they were all drowned," remarked MacFarland.

The whole front row now watched the professor narrowly. They knew already, with that keen perception that prayer sometimes gives, that this young teacher, ordained minister though he was, was up to no good.

"Who paid for these hogs?" demanded MacFarland suddenly.

"Well, er, the Bible doesn't say ..." began a plain-faced girl whose optimum future chances obviously lay along religious lines, but the prospective preacher indignantly rejected this evasion.

"Nobody paid for them," he said stoutly. "The evil spirits were responsible for drowning them. Why should anybody have had to pay for them?"

"Quite a blow to that farmer and his family," continued Mac-Farland philosophically. "Quite a loss—big mess of hogs—children didn't get any new shoes. Maybe they had to drop out of school, maybe they went hungry because a religious reformer came along and picked out their father's hogs to destroy."

"But Jesus didn't destroy their hogs," insisted the would-be minister. "The evil spirits did that."

"The Devil himself perhaps?" suggested MacFarland, but the prospective preacher would not be drawn into further argument and merely continued to look indignant.

"Well, do you suppose it was a case where human rights took precedence over property rights?" inquired MacFarland.

The whole front row nodded vigorously. The relief on the budding minister's face was evident.

"As in this revolution in Mexico?" asked the professor. "What is the theme, the *lema,* of those revolutionists?"

MacFarland now looked at me for the first time, as though he knew exactly what I was thinking.

"*Tierra y libertad,*" I said promptly.

MacFarland stared at me and then said slowly, "Yes, sir, and Mr. William Randolph Hearst's *tierra* too."

The next course I took with MacFarland was fifteen years later in the graduate school of the University of Oskaloosa, but in all those intervening years and in all the later years until Mac-Farland's death, I was always his student. He reached out with those Gadarene swine and put a permanent *wakan* on me. If he and I were young again and I was majoring, let us say, in physical chemistry and he was teaching a seminar on Vedic Hymnology I would sign up for the seminar.

Practical people may say at this point, "Why, that is romantic nonsense. In a university you study *subjects,* and you call them *disciplines* if you have the right background."

To which I reply, "There is more romantic nonsense dispensed about subjects and disciplines than about men in the universities. In an educational institution you study with men who use various subjects as educational instruments. The practical thing to do is to select your men and work with them in ferreting out the subjects you wish to use as instruments in your education."

During the year 1912–13 the University of the West was going through one of its periodic administrative crises. The president had labored for some years under the onus of not being an ordained minister. He was merely a Ph.D. in mathematics. Although by 1912 the school had long since declared itself nonsectarian, this was mostly window-dressing for the purpose of attracting students of other religious denominations than that which had founded the institution and still dominated it.

There was nothing wrong with President George Haskell's administration of the University of the West, as I can testify on the basis of later study of the institution's history. He was working hard but necessarily slowly to improve the quality of the faculty, an obvious first requirement for raising the level of instruction. This is always an agonizingly slow process in an American college when one has to start with a poor faculty. The most incompetent members of the faculty are the ones least likely to receive offers from other institutions. By the inexorable mechanics of academic democracy, chairmanships of committees, headships of departments, and other rewards of seniority thus tend to go to incompetents. This, in turn, stimulates the desires of abler members of the faculty to leave the institution. Since they are the ones who can get jobs elsewhere, they do leave. Nothing can stop this cyclic path to institutional demoralization except strong administrative action. To expect the faculty in such a case to provide the remedy is to be democratic to the point of an incredible naïveté. No faculty will police itself to that degree.

Against this tide at the University of the West, President Haskell fought heroically. He battled for funds to hold his competent faculty members and hire competent replacements for those whom he lost. The incompetents in their little positions of power opposed him slyly but nonetheless effectively. They wanted all faculty members paid strictly according to length of service in particular academic grades. The president, they said among themselves, was building up a personal empire and paying his young friends as much as senior professors were receiving. This, they agreed, was wrong.

Since the real reasons for the faculty opposition to the president would not bear public airing—indeed it could not stand continued scrutiny even in the faculty itself—it was necessary to fall back on the last refuge of an embattled professor in a Church-related college, religion. Word began to spread from anonymous yet "authoritative" sources that the president was not theologically "sound." How could you expect it? He was a mere mathematician who had no training of consequence even in philosophy, that queen of the disciplines. It was finally whispered that he saw no basic disagreement between modern science and Holy Writ. He had even ordered for the library Andrew D. White's "atheistical" work on *The History of the Warfare between Science and Theology.*

Professors undoubtedly started these accusations, but ministers of the gospel were the most active forces in spreading them and giving them substance. Most of these clergymen did not know President Haskell personally. He was not a popular public speaker. He did not appear on the same platforms with them. Of course he could not attend their ministerial conferences. Yet the clergymen not only of the university's founding sect but also of other denominations, most of which never sent students to the institution, seemed to be practically unanimous in regarding the president with a holy hatred.

I cannot begin to explain a phenomenon like this. As a non-minister, President Haskell held a position normally held by a clergyman, but it would seem that this circumstance alone was hardly sufficient to account for the widespread feeling against him among members of the clergy. Hell hath few furies like a man beaten out of a job that he regards as rightfully his, yet the great majority of these ministers must have known that under no conceivable conditions could they have become college presidents.

The senior faculty incompetents and their ministerial shock troops won. In March, 1913, President Haskell resigned. For the remainder of the academic year, the president's duties were performed by an administrative committee, headed by Professor John Calvin Pennington, chairman of the department of oratory. Thus, by a brilliant stroke of insight, the board of trustees negated the whole pattern of administration. The institution of the presidency was designed originally to furnish a single executive responsible for implementing the policies of the board. The board, itself a committee, now turned over the administrative function to another committee, so that any executive action would become difficult if not impossible.

I feel a temptation to digress here and give a lecture on the strengths and weaknesses of the system of lay boards of control in North American higher education. I resist the temptation. I know the real reason behind that temptation. I dislike telling what came next in this history. It was childish, stupid, and unnecessary, and I apply those adjectives to myself. But my ways were changed drastically by these events, and consequently I must report them.

As I mentioned earlier, Jim did not go out for track and could not go out for baseball, so he had more time than usual that spring of 1913. He spent some of it with a group of freshmen who came from the "big city" about twenty-five miles away. The city did not have 100,000 inhabitants, but still it was the only important center of population in a large area and it gave itself certain big-city airs.

I do not know anything that the big-city freshman group did

that was very bad. They went occasionally on week ends to a non-dry town about five miles away and daringly drank a few beers. Once in a while they dropped a paper bag full of water from the second floor of their dormitory onto some upperclassman's head, but in general they were moderately quiet boys.

About May 1 some of the big-city group had difficulties with their French instructor, a dapper young man who knew the French language but nothing much else to go with it.

One day some of the gang went to the basement of the building in which the French instructor held classes on the ground floor, armed themselves with cordwood sticks which were in plentiful supply for the wood-burning furnace, and suddenly pounded in unison on the floor in which the French class was being held. The girls in the class obligingly screamed at the tops of their lungs, the boys rushed outside for the purpose, they said, of capturing the perpetrators of this misdeed. Thus the bulk of the class period was consumed in non-linguistic activity.

I saw the students who probably did the pounding. I was in an alcove of the library stacks next door, and I observed six boys go into the basement. I noted who they were. I heard the pounding and saw the same six boys emerge from the basement. I made this observation carefully because I had warned Jim not to run around too much with that big-city outfit. I was checking on him. He was not with the gang on that occasion.

Jim and I had rooms at the house of a widow, Mrs. Collins, *née* Stewart, a cousin of Mr. Webster. We also kept our riding horses in Mrs. Collins' stable. She lived at the edge of the village about a half-mile from the college campus.

A little more than a week after the affair of the cordwood sticks, the administrative committee was investigating various matters and had come to that item in its agenda calling for consideration of this particular breach of discipline.

It was a Saturday morning. Jim was sleeping late. He had been out the night before with a girl. I knew about this because he had borrowed Rain-in-the-Face to serve as the lady's mount. The big black horse was now seventeen years old but still as beautiful as ever. It is needless to say that I prized him highly and seldom permitted him to go faster than a very sedate trot. He was much beloved by the girls, however, and he regarded them with affection, and occasionally I permitted Jim to borrow him for a slow, romantic *pasear*.

I had been working all morning on a theme for my English class. I heard Mrs. Collins answer the telephone in the kitchen, but I paid little attention to the circumstance. She was a sociable woman who made and received numerous telephone calls.

About ten o'clock Mrs. Collins asked me when I thought Jim might get up. I looked at my watch and said, "He ought to be up now. I'll roust him out."

Mrs. Collins then said casually that the people on the campus wanted to see him. They had called.

"Who wants to see him?" I asked.

"Professor Pennington," she replied.

"When did he call?"

"Oh, about an hour ago, or a little more. I guess maybe it was about eight-thirty."

I moved fast at this point and so did Jim as soon as I awakened him. While he was dressing I saddled his horse, and he left in a hurry without even a cup of coffee. He had no classes with Professor Pennington. Obviously it was the administrative committee that was calling for him.

When Jim reported on the campus he was immediately ushered into the president's office where the committee was holding its deliberations. The chairman asked Jim if he had taken part in pounding on the floor of the French classroom. Jim replied that he had not. The chairman then asked him if he knew who had done the pounding, and the boy said that he had a good idea who had done it. He was only seventeen years old, would not be eighteen until August, and he was accustomed to being frank.

Pennington next asked Jim for the names of the boys who had done this deed. Jim answered that he did not think it proper to give any names, that he had not seen the crime committed, and when he had said that he had a good idea who had done it he was referring merely to what he thought were his well-founded suspicions.

At this point the chairman chose to get tough. He demanded the names of those whom Jim suspected. Jim refused to give them. The other two members of the committee, a nonentity whose name I have forgotten and the dean of women whose name I remember all too well, prevailed upon the chairman not to make an issue of this point. They did not need more rumors and suspicions, they said. They had plenty of those; what they needed were facts.

As Jim was being dismissed, the dean of women said, "I do think, however, that Mr. Webster owes us an explanation of why it took him so long to obey our summons to this meeting."

If I could convey an adequate picture of this woman's preciously spinsterish voice and manner, it would be easy for any reader to understand Jim's instant resolution not to involve easygoing, unschooled Mrs. Collins in his answer. He merely replied stiffly that he had come to the campus as soon as possible after receiving the message that the committee wanted to see him.

"What we want to know," demanded Pennington, "in plain language, is why you didn't get here sooner."

"I came as soon as I could under the circumstances," said Jim.

"And what were those circumstances?" thundered the chairman.

Jim declined to give them.

The committee told him to wait outside, deliberated a few minutes, and then called him back to inform him that he was suspended for one week, at the end of which time he would be expected to apologize to the committee and to explain fully the reasons for taking almost two hours to answer the committee's telephoned summons.

Jim was a troubled boy when he reported all this in detail to me. I was even more troubled. I felt that I had neglected in some important way my duties as an elder brother. It seemed to me that if I could explain matters to the committee myself, it would be a contribution to the welfare of the boy and of the institution.

I went to the campus on foot, and I made it about as fast as I would if I had stopped to saddle my horse. The committee had adjourned. I went immediately to the chairman's house. He was, I suppose, at lunch. At least he came into the front parlor with a napkin in his hand and a look of impatience on his face.

I said that I would like the privilege of appearing before the committee. He said that the committee would not meet again until the next Saturday, one week from that time. I asked whether it was possible to have a special meeting of the committee. He said that it was not possible.

"What do you want to see the committee about?" he asked.

"About the case of James Webster," I said.

"What is your interest in that case?" he demanded.

"Why, he is my brother," I explained.

"But your name is Peddiwell," said Pennington coldly. I am sure now that he knew very well my relationship to Mr. Webster and to Jim. But I described the relationship, and then I said I thought I could explain why Jim was late in answering the committee's summons.

"It is up to him to explain that," said Pennington. "You are just attempting to interfere in matters that do not concern you."

At this juncture I sought to make the point that the real question was whether Jim had been involved in the prank the committee was investigating. I knew very certainly that he had not been involved in it, I said.

Of course, the professor wanted to know how I could be so sure. I said that I had seen the boys. I recounted the circumstance and pointed out the probability that they were the ones responsible. I could not be sure that all of them had pounded on the floor, but I knew that Jim was not among them and therefore could not have been guilty.

Pennington demanded the names of the group I had seen go into the basement. I do not know why that surprised me. Jim had just told me of the same demand on him, but perhaps I felt that my greater maturity made the request even more unreasonable.

"I cannot understand why you would make that request," I said.

"Oh, you can't, huh?" snarled Pennington, thoroughly angered. "Maybe that's because *you* were one of the guilty!"

"Listen, Mister," I said, angry myself, "I have no interest in those damn' baby tricks except to see that my younger brother was not involved in them."

Pennington reacted with shocked fury. "Swearing at me? Profanity! This is one thing that the University of the West will not countenance!"

"I believe I just said *damn*," I remarked in what I thought was a pacific manner, "and I certainly apologize to you and the university for that."

The professor's rage only increased. He ordered me out of his house.

The committee met that afternoon in special session and expelled me for cursing the chief executive of the university. Appearing in my own defense, I said again that I apologized to the professor and the university for using the word *damn*. Unfortunately I added that I did not know what else to offer to do unless the chairman wanted me to kiss his hand. I was willing to do that, I said, and throw the hands of the rest of the committee into the bargain.

I have no excuse to proffer for my share in this painful incident.

Jim went to a good, state university as a result of the affair, and I enlisted in the United States Regular Army. Thus higher education and national defense both benefited from my errors.

This experience was instructive. It taught me to regard myself as a poor mediator, and since May, 1913, I have always tried to avoid the role.

TEN

School of the Regiment

I SHALL NOT MENTION the number of my first regiment. Any old-timer will be able to identify it from my description, and any new-timer who may read this will not care what regiment it was. I will merely say, therefore, that it was the best regiment of infantry in the United States Regular Army in the days when that army was for its size the best in the world.

In those days recruits were trained in the regiment in which they were to serve. Nowadays they are trained by specialists in recruit depots of one kind and another and are then assigned to a unit so that they can go into action the first time under the command of officers and noncommissioned officers whom they have never seen before.

I am not going to detail the various aspects of training a recruit in the regiment. I can sum up the process by saying that the main purpose was to develop in the recruit a few key attitudes. The technical skills and information he needed were then acquired in support of those attitudes.

Nowadays, I suppose, for example, that recruits may take a kitchen-police course in their training camps. I do not know that they do, you understand, but it would be a logical move. In my old regiment we had to learn skills like that on the job.

In some ways this is a poor example for me to cite. In my

eight years of military service, about half of which was as an enlisted man, I was on kitchen police only once. I practiced only one
skill, that of cleaning pans which had been used over open fires.
This happened because I chose to be brave.

The regiment was on the Mexican Border. The sun was just
rising as we stood reveille, and it was already hotter than the
proverbial hinges.

The company commander took the report in his usual fashion, but after returning the salute, instead of saying, "First Sergeant, dismiss the company," he said, "At ease," and then proceeded to explain in a kindly way that he wanted volunteers for a
special duty. He did not say that the duty would be dangerous,
but I assumed immediately that it would be. In all the fictional
accounts that I had ever read about officers calling for volunteers,
some deed of daring was in the making.

"When I give the word of command," said the captain, "any
volunteer will step one pace to the front. Company, *attention!*
Volunteers, one pace forward, *march!*"

Without the slightest hesitation, I stepped forward. It
seemed an easy way to begin distinguishing myself in the regiment. I expected to be accompanied by at least a dozen fellow volunteers, but to my surprise the company commander spoke at once
in the singular. "Take that man's name, First Sergeant," he said
crisply, "and dismiss the company."

The first sergeant told me to go to the regimental headquar-
ters immediately after breakfast. He gave me the name of the
noncommissioned officer to whom I was to report.

This noncommissioned officer was the most mournful-looking
sergeant I have ever seen. I do not know whether his sad countenance and manner were habitual or were merely associated with
that particular day and duty. I never saw him again after that
day to my knowledge. He was clearly a man of long service and I
assumed that he was not a volunteer for this duty. I had a feeling
indeed as I looked around at the other men assembled for the
duty that I was the only volunteer.

There were twelve of us privates, one from each rifle company, a corporal from the machine-gun company, and the sad sergeant. The latter wore a Company D collar ornament, and he spoke several times with peculiar acrimony to the private from that company. He recited the equipment and weapons we would take with us. He did this slowly, lugubriously, almost as though intoning a service for the dead. "Rifle," he said, "bayonet, entrenching tool, full canteen, 180 rounds of ammunition, one can of tomatoes, one package of hardtack, one shelter half, one blanket. Repeat it," he snarled at the man from Company D who complied stumblingly as though hating every item in the list. Then the sergeant said, "Be here at seven o'clock. We're goin' on scout duty and we'll be gone all day. Any questions?"

The term *scout duty* caught my interest. I had seen a small column of horsemen in the hills several days earlier and had been told by my corporal that it was a scout detail. Undoubtedly it was what we would now call a reconnaissance troop from some horse outfit, but in my naïve recruit fashion I had the idea that scout details were generally mounted. The only one I had ever seen had been mounted, and all the stories I could remember about scouts had them on horseback. When the sad sergeant asked for questions, therefore, it seemed possible to me that he had assumed that we knew where to draw our horses, that everybody but me did know, and so I asked about it.

The sergeant's sadness disappeared for a moment under a great cloud of incredulity. Then he lapsed once more into deep mourning.

"Horses?" he said. "Horses? What in the God-damn' hell do you want of horses? Ain't you an infantryman? No, you ain't. You're just a no-good, God-damn' John. We ain't never had such dumb Johns in this regiment since Pontius P. Pilate was a lance-corporal. Horses! Jesus H. Christopher Columbus Christ! Dismissed, until seven o'clock!"

The duty was simple. We marched along the Border for about ten miles from our camp, pitched our shelter tents, cut open the cans and consumed our tomatoes and hardtack, emptied the sand from our shoes, adjusted our socks, and then marched

back again. We did not march fast, and our load was light. With
rifle and ammunition included the pack did not weigh over
twenty pounds as compared with the full pack of sixty pounds.

But I was tired when we reached camp, and as soon as we
were dismissed I rushed to my company street and crawled into
my shelter tent. I lay there cleaning my rifle as the bugles
sounded first call for retreat, but I made no move to respond to
the call. I supposed that my detail to scout duty exempted me
from that formation.

My corporal came along and disabused me of the notion. He
was always courteous but direct and clear. "Makes no difference,"
he said. "If you're here when the call sounds, you stand retreat."

As I fell into the rear rank of my squad, I felt relieved that I
had cleaned all the dust off my rifle and had wiped out the bore.
Always before, at the retreat formation, the company commander
had taken the opportunity to inspect rifles. But this time after
open ranks and *prepare for inspection* were given, he walked
along the ranks looking only at shoes. He said nothing until he
came to me. I brought my rifle up to *inspection arms*. He looked
at my feet and inquired courteously, "Why aren't your shoes
shined?"

I explained that I had been on dismounted scout duty all
day, that I had just returned shortly before the bugles sounded
first call for retreat, and that I had therefore had no time to shine
my shoes. During the explanation I was thinking that the captain
should know all this without having to be told. After all, he had
seen me volunteer at reveille.

The captain listened patiently to my explanation and then
said, "First Sergeant, put this man on kitchen police."

During the retreat I paid little attention to the ceremony.
Even the beautiful bugle music, *To the Colors,* was just background for my bitter reflections. As soon as the company was dismissed, I approached the first sergeant and complained that I
could not see why I was put on kitchen police for not having my
shoes shined when I had been on scout duty all day and had returned to camp just before the call for retreat was sounded.

"You was not put on k.p. for havin' dirty shoes," said the sergeant.

"I wasn't?" I asked. "Well, what the hell was I put on k.p. for, then?"

"You was put on k.p. for alibi-in'," said the first sergeant. "You probably don't know what alibi-in' is, but you'll have plenty of time to figure it out because you'll be on k.p. quite a spell."

As a criminal kitchen police I was given the worst job, cleaning pans. There were many of them, and each one had to be scraped, scrubbed, and polished to inspection brightness. I worked through the evening by the light of a candle into which moths made suicidal dives. *Call to quarters, tattoo,* and then *taps* were sounded while I still labored on. I do not know at what time I finished the pans, as I had no watch, but it must have been well after midnight, since reliefs of the guard were changed twice after taps before I ended my toil.

When at last I crawled onto my blanket I was very tired and very hot. I took off all my clothing, put my rifle and belt beside me, placed my shoes upside down to keep out crawling things, and went to sleep instantaneously. It seemed only seconds later that I was awakened by someone stepping on my feet as they protruded from my shelter tent. All the bugles in the regiment were sounding a call that I had never heard before. They were not playing in unison; each of them was repeating the call at will. I heard the first sergeant say, "Company M, fall in!" I jumped into my shoes, grabbed my rifle and belt, and galloped out into the darkness as I heard the company commander sing out, "Right by squads, double time, march!" I rushed up to the column crying, "Corporal Rinehart, Corporal Rinehart!" To my infinite relief the corporal answered, "Here, Ab, right in here," reached out, and pulled me into the squad.

The bugles had been sounding, *To Arms.* It was a surprise "attack" started by some trigger-happy pickets in the Mexican force which lay across the border from us, but it was really just a training exercise. We double-timed out into the desert, deployed as skirmishers, and maneuvered around for a couple of hours. When we were first ordered, *Down,* I just got down on my hands and knees. The sand-burs and little cacti were plentiful on that terrain, and I shrank from meeting them full-length. It seemed to me so dark, moreover, that one rifleman on his hands and knees among 2,000 prone men would not be noticeable. I was wrong. A sharp-eyed lieutenant cried piteously, "Get that man down up there!" and my corporal said, "Is that you, Ab? For Christ's sake, get down!" So I got right down for Corporal Rinehart's sake. I thought the world of him, and I proved it as my belly hit those sand-burs.

Finally dawn approached, and we moved into column of squads and started back to camp. Now that it was getting pretty light my clotheslessness was beginning to be generally noticed, and I was subjected to a considerable amount of derision. I remember well that even though I was only a recruit I recognized the value of this joking. It was a definite stage toward making me a real member of the regiment. So I walked along at the route step, jauntily picking cactus spines and sand-burs from my person and feeling happy.

Then I saw the company commander standing at the left of the column, looking over each rank of four as it passed. Since I was number four in my rank, I would pass right next to him. He could hardly overlook my being clothed only in belt and shoes. I thought, *I'll be on k.p. forever, but what the hell.* The last phrase of that thought indicated an important step forward in my military education.

As we came to where the captain was standing, although we were still at *route step,* I marched more or less automatically at attention and stared straight ahead. The company commander turned and started marching along beside me.

"Where are your clothes?" he asked in his usual polite manner.

"In my shelter-tent, sir," I replied.

"Why haven't you got them on?" he persisted.

I was not a particularly bright boy and certainly not well fitted for professional soldiering. I could easily have given the wrong answer that morning and explained everything. But my guardian angel or perhaps the mere fact that I felt wonderful saved me.

"Just carelessness, sir," I said.

The captain halted, did a right face, and resumed inspecting the column.

When I reported for kitchen duty at breakfast, the mess sergeant refused my services. "You ain't on k.p. no more," he said. "The first sergeant took you off as soon as the regiment come in from the field this morning."

I asked for no explanation. I was never on kitchen police again, and I think I was never even suspected again in the Army of alibi-ing. I will not testify as to my record in this regard in civil life. The transfer between the two environments is often not great.

We studied subjects sometimes in the regiment, just as they do in the colleges and universities. My platoon sergeant, for example, was a history teacher. At least, he used as an instrument of instruction what he claimed was history, perhaps even thought was history.

After about three months of operating somewhat independently, the regiment was assembled with two other infantry regiments, a squadron of cavalry, and two battalions of field artillery into a single field force. For the first time, therefore, I was enabled to observe other outfits passing in review. The differences displayed by the horse outfits were understandable. One could see why the artillery drivers did not do eyes right when passing the reviewing stand, for instance. The other infantry regiments showed what was more difficult to understand. They passed in review without fixing bayonets. In our regiment the command would come, *Pass the regiment in review,* and then our colonel would sing out, *Fix Bayonets.* I had assumed that this was the usual infantry practice, but here were these other infantry outfits passing the reviewing stand with only their rifle muzzles to keep aligned. It seemed to me that we were at a disadvantage, and so I asked my sergeant the reason for the difference.

"It's because we can be whipped," he said and went on to give his lecture. "This outfit was begun in the Continental Army under the command of an officer named Anthony Wayne. We was whipped at Germantown, just outside of Philadelphia, where the British Grenadier Guards cut hell out of us in the fog. We throwed away our weapons and run like stuck pigs, squealin' for quarter. Mad Anthony cried and broke his sword and tried to get General Washington to accept his resignation. Washington wouldn't take it, but he put us to guardin' wagons. He didn't trust us much, and you can't blame him.

"Then at Brandywine we got another chance. We was on the American right flank, and the visibility was bad again, but that's no excuse. We was nervous, tryin' to show we amounted to somethin'. We went forward too fast, swung around to our left, and fired into our own troops. Then when the British come in with the cold steel, we broke and run again. After that we guarded wagons all the time. We was the dregs of the Continentalers.

"Then come Valley Forge. Durin' that winter there come a shipment of Spanish bayonets from New Orleans to Pittsburgh by water and then overland by packhorses. Baron von Steuben, who kinda liked us for no good reason that I can see except we was underdogs, got enough bayonets to equip us. We had no bayonet lugs on our guns, but the old Baron, he showed us how to bind them bayonets on the muzzles with strips of green rawhide which tightened up like iron. He gave us bayonet drill. We took to it and liked it. We was always practicin' lunges, thrusts, and parries. We never had to learn to fix and unfix our bayonets. They was fixed all the time.

"Then when General Washington decided to take Stony Point, for some God-damn' reason nobody could figure he told Wayne to take the place with us. Old Anthony come out that mornin', called us to attention, and told us the assignment. 'We'll go in tonight,' he said. 'It'll be pitch dark, and I want every man of you to wear a white rag around his left arm. You'll have your guns unloaded and you'll take that place with the bayonet. When you see a man with no white rag on his arm, slap the steel into him.' Then he kinda sashayed off to one side. We broke attention, we laid our guns down careful so's not to nick the bayonets, and then we begun to turn handsprings. We took the Point that night against a superior British force behind breastworks. We killed or captured every God-damn' lobster-back in the place. That British outfit was the Grenadier Guards.

"As a regiment, we have never been whipped since. We led the assault on the gate at Mexico City. We come off the field at First Bull Run in a hollow square with our colors and supportin' field guns in the center, and our sergeants countin' cadence for the parade step. We're good and we know it, but we ain't perfect. We have to pass in review with fixed bayonets, the only regiment in the Army that does it, because we gotta remind ourselves that we can be whipped, that we have been whipped, but that when our bayonets are fixed, by God, we can't be whipped!"

I never heard those commands again, *Pass the regiment in review, Fix bayonets!* without the fierce consciousness flooding my being, *When our bayonets are fixed, we cannot be whipped.*

The last time I saw that regiment pass in review, I was merely an elderly civilian in the audience. I heard a woman say, "My! They move like clockwork."

The amateur in education might say at this point, "We have to analyze that activity pretty carefully and teach each part systematically, insisting on perfect mastery."

But the professional laughs sardonically and thinks, *Sure, sure, but why attempt to explain it? This is something you learn in one flashing gestalt, or you never learn it.*

ELEVEN

Sergeant Cobb's Campaign

TO THE OCCASIONAL CITIZEN who nowadays mentions to me the 1916 Punitive Expedition into Mexico, it is usually "that time you were trying to catch Pancho Villa." To students of international relations, it is no doubt sometimes regarded as a move of pawns in a game between Woodrow Wilson and the various revolutionary and counter-revolutionary forces south of the Rio Grande. To specialists in the history of World War I, it may be looked upon as a field-training exercise for the United States Army before it was put into war against the German Empire.

Now that I have to examine my own participation in this affair, I find that all the foregoing conceptions are foreign to me. I never saw General Francisco Villa in 1916 or any other time. I knew next to nothing about the relations between the Woodrow Wilson and Venustiano Carranza governments, and in this regard I was little different from members of the United States Congress. I was not aware that we were about to enter the war against Germany. Why should I have been? A national presidential campaign was being waged and won that summer under the slogan, "He kept us out of war."

In my memory, therefore, the Punitive Expedition remains a strictly personal affair. To me it will always be Sergeant Cobb's campaign.

I first met Cobb in 1914 when he was still a private, and I was just emerging from recruithood. I was on a week-end pass in the big city when I entered a saloon, not so much out of thirst, I insist, as curiosity. Grunts, oaths, and the sound of breaking furniture came over the swinging doors as I entered the room. A slender, blond man in Army uniform, wearing the scarlet hatcord of the field artillery, was standing with his back to a pool table along the wall opposite the bar. He held in his hands the remnants of a demolished chair. Three civilians, all armed with pool cues, were deployed before him. One was a fairly large man whose nose was bleeding a little. A second was almost as big but bore no marks of recent combat. The third, a smaller, rat-faced character, was sidling toward the end of the pool table with the evident intention of enveloping the field artillery. He carried in his left hand the neck of a broken bottle to supplement the cue in his right hand.

A dozen other occupants of the room, all civilians, were lined with their backs in audience fashion against the bar. The single bartender, an overweight individual, was calmly wiping beer foam off the mahogany. It was this last fact, I think, that gave me final basis for decision. Obviously the artilleryman was going to be severely punished, and nobody in that saloon intended to interfere. I did not enter this quarrel impulsively. I thought all these items over. I was particularly aware of the picture of that fat bartender making no move to get out his sawed-off shotgun and restore order. Thought, under pressure, however, can be practically instantaneous.

"Hold it, you birds," I said. "If this is a fight, *one* of you fight him and the other two act as seconds. I will be the artilleryman's second."

"Keep out of this, tin soldier," said the man with the bloody nose, turning his head to look at me over his right shoulder.

By this time I was within one long step of him. He was not only the biggest of the three but also, apparently, their leader. Again, my decision was made very rapidly, and it was speeded up by the man's unfortunate choice of epithet. I wore the blue hatcord of the infantry. One look at my collar ornament was enough to tell any literate observer that I was a member of an élite regiment of the United States Regular Army. Few things the man could have said would have insured more thoroughly his ensuing unconsciousness. I was angry when I put a solid right hook on the angle of his jaw as he turned his head. I knew when the blow landed that the odds in this fight were now even and would remain so for a considerable period.

I turned quickly to take my share of the two remaining men, but they were both backing away. I glanced at the artilleryman, for the first time looking closely at him. To my astonishment, he was smiling easily as though someone had just coined a *bon mot*, but he spoke with sober crispness to the burly bartender who had now dropped his towel and was reaching underneath the counter and mumbling something about no fighting being allowed inside the saloon.

"Keep yore hands on top of that wood," ordered the soldier, and the bartender promptly complied.

"Ah notice it wasn't fightin'," continued the artilleryman, "so long as *yore* friends were gangin' up on me, but when *mah* friend steps into it and sends that big jasper bye-bye, why then it's naughty. Now, Ah want to tell you somethin'. You keep on the way you been goin' lately, and you can get this place took apart by experts, and Ah mean wagon soldiers."

While this advice was being given, the easy smile never left the artilleryman's lips, but his eyes remained somber. Then he glanced at me, and his eyes softened a little. "I'm obliged to the infantry," he said, "and it would pleasure me to testify to it by purchasin' you a drink."

"I could stand a tonic of some kind to restore my shattered nerves," I admitted, "but I would prefer, if you don't mind, being served by some person not quite so fat in head as well as in body." I was still unpleasantly conscious of that shotgun under the bar.

"Soldier, Ah sympathize with yore delicate feelin's," said the artilleryman, "and Ah hasten to follow yore desires."

As we left the place I noted, with relief, that the man with the bloodied nose was now clearly conscious. The angle at which his head was turned when he was struck could have been unfortunate for him, but luckily his neck vertebrae were well articulated.

The artilleryman was William B. Cobb. "The *B* is for *Bowie,* my mother's maiden name," he explained. "She was from Prince George's County, Maryland, where the Bowies are thick as fleas. Ah've never been there myself. Ah was born in Virginia but still a long ways from Maryland, way down southwest on a little farm between Radford and Pulaski. Ah took the President's two-bit piece, you might say, when Ah was young. Ah joined the cavalry at first. That was pretty near five years ago. In my second hitch Ah went over to the field artillery. You get a change from groomin' hosses all the time. You groom the hosses all right, and then you go over and polish up the guns and caissons too. It's like the song says;

> The Cavalree for braveree,
> The Infantry for guts,
> Th' Artillery for slavery,
> And the Medical Corps for nuts.
> It's home, boys, home,
> It's home we want to be,
> And the grass grows green
> In North Amerikee."

Cobb spoke with a strong southwestern Virginia accent. He never put a final *g* on a present participle, and he pronounced *can't* to rhyme with *paint*. His speech, however, was not at all that of an unschooled man. He never mentioned any academic experience to me, and I did not interrogate him on such matters.

I can say of Cobb that he made friends very quickly but not often. He became my friend, I think, not so much from gratitude as from interest in the mode of my entrance into the El Paso saloon imbroglio. He showed little interest in his own fight that had preceded my appearance.

"That beefy person you hit is the bouncer in that joint," he explained negligently. "He is also the dice expert. We were rollin' 'em on that pool table when Ah got suspicious those boys were switchin' educated cubes on me. In the argument, they got those cues out of the rack and Ah had nothin' but that chair. It was sort of flimsy," he added apologetically. "What Ah liked to see was yore right hand move just that short distance and then explode when it landed."

Cobb suspected me of being a professional fighter, but he would not ask me whether I was. He never asked a friend questions that might be embarrassing. To do so would have violated some article of his personal code. I assured him earnestly that I was not a fighter, but he misunderstood me.

"Ah can see that," he said comfortably, "and it's just as well for the population that you don't have to play like you're a fighter very often."

Not long after Cobb and I became acquainted he was promoted to corporal. It was almost as spectacular as a battle-field promotion. In all the military units of the El Paso area, the story was a favorite one.

Cobb was on mounted guard one evening riding a sentry post that ran for three hundred yards along one side of the parade ground. It was after call to quarters. It had been raining heavily, but the rain had stopped and the moon had started peering through the broken clouds when Cobb heard a horseman splashing across the parade ground. He cantered over to intercept the traveler and, at fifty yards, drew his pistol and challenged in proper fashion, "Halt! Dismount!"

The horseman halted but did not dismount. "Sentry," he called, "will you let me move my horse forward about six feet? You've halted me right in a mud puddle."

The officer of the day for that guard was a new commander of one of the batteries in Cobb's regiment. He had the reputation of being hard and sly. Cobb had no doubt that this was the person whom he had halted and that the captain was shrewdly testing the sentries to see whether they knew their duty.

"Dismount!" repeated Cobb sharply.

"Sentry," said the rider, still remaining on his horse, "you

don't have to let me advance. I can back my horse out of this
puddle."

"Are you goin' to get off that hoss, or am Ah goin' to have to
blow you off?" inquired Cobb.

The horseman dismounted promptly.

"Who's there?" called Cobb.

"Commanding General," came the answer.

"Advance, dismounted, Commandin' General, to be recognized," directed Cobb, and the general led his horse forward until
the sentry halted him again at six paces. Cobb leaned over, scru-
tinized him carefully in the dim moonlight, and, finally satisfied,
said, "Mount, Commandin' General, and pass."

The general mounted and then asked, "What post is this,
Sentry?"

"Number five, sir," replied Cobb. As he answered, he wondered for a moment whether the general wanted that information
for a purpose unfriendly to him, but promptly rejected the
thought. The old man's character was all against any such development.

Cobb was right in that judgment, but did not foresee the
general's positive reaction to the incident. The old man rode directly to the guardhouse, asked the commander of the guard for
the name, organization, and length of service of the sentry on
post number five, and then sent his compliments to Cobb's battery commander with the suggestion that as soon as a vacancy
occurred, if the man had no severe disciplinary marks against
him, he would make a good noncommissioned officer.

Cobb was a corporal only a little over a year when he was
transferred to a newly organized pack artillery outfit. When his
battalion entered Mexico in the spring of 1916 he was made sergeant and was acting battalion sergeant-major.

My own entrance into Mexico was neither as a foot soldier nor
a horse soldier but as a mule soldier. The problems of transport
were so pressing that men who could drive a four-mule-team
wagon were in short supply. I found myself, infantryman, expert
rifleman (so it said on the payroll where I drew extra money for

the rating), riding on the seat of a canvas-covered wagon loaded with hay, oats, and rations, and driving four mules.

Let no one suppose that I was ashamed of being a mule-driver. I was proud of it. Although I do not pretend to know mules and understand them as I do horses, I have a profound respect for them. They have stronger intellects than horses, and perhaps that is why they are often harder to handle. They are more powerful, pound for pound, and much tougher than horses.

The four mules I drove in Cobb's campaign, Bill and Ben, the wiry, shrewd, little leaders, and Mack and Moses, the imperturbable and husky wheelers, were animals I am honored to have been associated with. There was not one of them who had the slightest streak of meanness in him, yet any of them, under certain conditions, would kick first and ask questions afterward.

Water was often scarce and carefully doled out on our trips. Horses would paw and nicker anxiously when they saw water buckets being carried to the column from the tank wagon. My mules never lifted a hoof or wasted a breath on pleas for water. They knew I would give them their share and maybe a little bit more. As a matter of fact, I carried in my wagon without orders a fifteen-gallon keg of water as an emergency canteen for my mules. They did not mind pulling that small extra weight as an insurance against thirst.

I mention Bill, Ben, Mack, and Moses thus specifically because they were definite educational influences on me. Just as horse soldiers and mounted policemen have somewhat different personalities from those of foot-soldiers and ordinary cops, so a mule-driver tends to become different from his horse-driving colleagues. You work with those intelligent, calm, determined animals day after day, and you will find that you are trying a little harder yourself to be intelligent, calm, and determined.

If I may be allowed to digress so far for a moment, I was in 1919 in Germany the officer in charge of dipping hundreds of horses and mules to cure them of the mange. I was still suffering from certain injuries, and so my part in the project was merely supervisory. I thus had plenty of opportunity to study the animals as they took their treatment.

The veterinarians prepared an evil-smelling brew in a big vat in an idle German textile factory. The engineers rigged up a cage that could be raised and lowered with a donkey engine and block and tackle. The animal was led up a gang plank into the cage. The door was shut behind him. Then he was lowered into the steaming medicine until his head went under. He was next drawn out of the liquid, a door was opened in front of him, and he was brought forward on another gang plank to safety.

The typical horse fought in terror against entering this cage. He saw it for what it was, a trap, but he was forced into it by the soldiers. Then, when the cage entered the medicine, the horse, wild-eyed, struggled to break out, even to crawl through the roof. Sometimes he screamed as the liquid came up around his throat. When he was released from the cage he shivered pitiably and went to the nearest soldier for sympathy and kind words.

The typical mule entered the cage suspiciously but without fighting. He could see that he had to go in. There were too many soldiers at hand for him to hope to break through their cordon. As the medicine came up his neck, he watched it with ears forward. He made no attempt to break out of the cage. He could see it was too strong. He went under the surface, well braced, his body stiffened, with no sign of fear, but you could see the anger building up in him. The soldiers always put two halter shanks on the mule before opening the cage door, so that he would have a man on each side of him, for he was likely to come charging out with front hooves flying and try to kill the nearest soldier to pay for the gross indignity just put upon him.

Bill and Ben would both have come out of the cage charging like that. Moses would not have done so. He was so wise that he would probably have controlled his temper. I do not know what Mack would have done. He had a streak of Celtic unpredictability in his personality.

Sergeant's Cobb's battalion was under the command of Ma-

jor Bellows, the one whom the jackass-battery soldiers called
Hole-in-the-Head Bellows. According to them he was shot in the
head during the Moro campaign in the Philippines. There was a
hole just above his left ear, they said, covered by a silver plate.
As temperatures fluctuated, this plate was sometimes hotter and
sometimes colder than the surrounding bone tissue. This caused
the major to have mental aberrations. It was possible for him to
be normal only when the bone temperature and the silver temperature were exactly the same. This did not happen often.

I give merely the enlisted men's story and diagnosis of this
case. My own observation led me to believe that Bellows was
crazy all the time, and he may never have been wounded. I served
under him briefly myself in World War I.

One very hot day Major Bellows marched his battalion so far
that the pack-mules were lying down and refusing to get up. The
infantry column on the right had halted an hour earlier. The cavalry column on the left was just going into camp. Bellows insisted
on whipping the mules to their feet and proceeding with the
march.

Sergeant Cobb, ranking noncommissioned officer and, indeed,
next to the major in rank at that particular place and time, since
the two lieutenants of the battalion were keeping discreetly to the
rear of the column, politely called Bellows' attention to the cavalry halting for the night. The major said, "Are you trying to tell
me to halt?"

"No, sir," said the sergeant, "Ah just thought maybe the major didn't notice what the cavalry were doin'."

The major glared at Cobb and then said to a corporal standing near a prostrate mule, "Whip that God-damned animal to his
feet!"

"He won't get up, sir," said the corporal. "You can kill him,
but he won't get up."

It is my own opinion that the major was so disordered in his
mind that the word *kill* triggered his reaction. He drew his pistol
on the corporal. Cobb, standing on the off-side of the major's
horse, caught the officer's wrist with his left hand and took the

pistol in his right hand, his thumb in front of the hammer so that
the weapon could not be fired. Bellows dismounted and collapsed.
Cobb reported immediately to the frightened lieutenants. The
major had the sergeant put in arrest and charged him with direct
disobedience of orders in the face of the enemy, mutiny, and personal violence against an officer.

Sergeant Cobb told the court-martial that he reached instinc-
tively for the major's wrist and took his pistol to keep him from
shooting the corporal when he, the major, was obviously not in
his right mind. The enlisted witnesses substantiated Cobb's story
at every point.

I have nothing but contempt for the lieutenants, both graduates of and a disgrace to the United States Military Academy.
They had deliberately absented themselves when they saw trouble
brewing, and in the court-martial they testified that the major
appeared normal to them. I am also not impressed by the ability
and honesty of the officer assigned to act as Cobb's defense counsel. He should have put his commission on the line, if necessary,
in demanding that Bellows be examined by psychiatrists (or
alienists as they were then called).

Cobb was reduced to the ranks, dishonorably discharged, and
given five years' imprisonment in the Disciplinary Barracks at
Fort Leavenworth. He served almost two years of the sentence,
when a secretary of war, who was a lawyer, on recommendation
of a first lieutenant, who was a school teacher, removed Cobb's
dishonorable discharge, restored him to duty, and permitted him
to finish his enlistment.

I am proud to say that Cobb was assigned to my battery in
France in 1918 and was promptly promoted to sergeant and made
chief of a gun section. I never knew a finer soldier or more complete gentleman of any grade or function in the United States
Army.

TWELVE

Toot Sweet's War

WHEN THE UNITED STATES declared war on Germany on April 6, 1917, I had been enjoying civilian life for three months since finishing my first enlistment in the Army. I was almost immediately given that kind of directive which thirty years later was called "an invitational order." It was a telephone message asking me to take an examination for a commission as second lieutenant in the newly authorized Officers Reserve Corps.

I passed the examination and was ordered to report as an instructor in the First Officers Training Camp at the Presidio of San Francisco. At the end of the camp I was put on inactive duty to await the formation of the regiments of drafted troops that were being assembled in that summer of 1917.

I was impatient. I felt that if I were assigned to a drafted regiment I would be likely to serve throughout the war as a drill instructor. So, after checking with the camp adjutant to make sure there was no regulation against a reserve officer on inactive duty enlisting in the Regular Army, I went to the nearest recruiting station and joined the field artillery. Early in the fall of 1917 I was in France with one of the first American units to enter the country.

My division took part in four major engagements and one defensive sector in France in 1917–18. I was in all of them, and so was my favorite Army horse. Since he was more spectacular than

I and since he was fifteen years younger than I and therefore presumably more amenable to instruction, I will tell of some of his
educational experiences in that war and refer to my own learnings
as they related incidentally to him.

I first met this animal on a brilliant moonlight night when
the regiment was on a practice march. At one of the halts, a cannoneer said, "There's a sick horse down in *F* Battery. They're
tryin' to find the veterinarian."

I walked along the column, leading my own single-mount,
until I came to the patient.

He was lying in the road, under saddle with full pack, groaning occasionally. I leaned over to look at him. I was struck by his
color, buckskin, and his Roman nose. I noted also that his eyes
were open and that he rolled them in a curious manner. His
groans, moreover, appeared to have meretricious overtones.

"I don't believe he is sick," I said to the chief of section
whose single-mount the animal was.

"Well, what's he down in the road for, then?" asked the sergeant worriedly.

"He may be malingering," I suggested. Just then the
veterinarian, a bustling major with a noticeable *embonpoint*, hurried up and took immediate charge.

"Come on men," he said. "Get this sick animal on his feet, or
he'll die. Grab him by the tail," he added to me.

"I don't know him personally, sir," I said, "but I'm willing
to pull on his halter shank," and I took hold of that item.

"Good Lord," puffed the major, "afraid of a sick horse!"
Then he seized the animal's tail and pulled sidewise on it.

I did not have time to pull on the halter shank, and no one
else had as yet attached themselves to the horse or his equipment,
when he got to his feet like a cat and in the same swift movement
put both his hind shoes in the veterinarian's stomach. Apparently
he resented having his tail jerked sidewise.

Fortunately, the officer was fairly close to the hindquarters
when the blow was struck, and he was not severely injured. He
rode back to camp in an ambulance that night and was returned

to duty in three or four days, although he continued to walk in a slightly bowed attitude for about a week longer.

I desire to record here my respect for the major. He was a good veterinarian, a V.M.D. from a famous Eastern state university. One cannot blame either him or the university for his failure to diagnose completely the big buckskin's difficulty. I regret to add, however, that the major never appeared to care for me after this incident. Perhaps he derived a psychic scar of some kind from it. If so, it was understandable that I should be tied to it in his mind.

One of the cannoneers of my section, a large boy of Swedish origin named Lundborg, who spoke G.I. French as well as English with musical intonations, christened that horse for me as we walked back to our battery. "At first he did not vant to get op," mused Lundborg tunefully, "but ven he did get op, he sure as hell got op *toot sveet !*"

I traded for Toot Sweet the next day. I rode my current single-mount, a beautiful, black, English horse, over to *F* Battery and soon spotted that Roman-nosed buckskin on the picket line. When I saw an Oregon brand on his near hip, a brand from the Ochoco Valley, a sudden nostalgia clutched my throat. That horse had been foaled on the ranch just south of Mr. Webster's Jay-Jay range. I took a deep breath and set myself to hide my emotion.

"So that's the trouble-maker?" I remarked inquiringly to the section chief who had been riding the animal the night before.

"He *is* a mean bastard," admitted the sergeant morosely.

I tried to look at the Ochoco buckskin matter-of-factly, but to my astonishment all I could see was Mr. Webster. I was unable, at least for the moment, to dicker. "I'll give you this black horse for him," I offered swiftly.

The *F*-Battery noncommissioned officer's shocked reaction brought me back to reality. He had obviously nourished no hope like this, but in the best trading tradition he rallied to defense of his animal. "I tell you, mister," he said stoutly, "that buckskin is a mighty good single-mount."

"Yeah," I replied scornfully, "except when he lies down under full pack, groaning that he's about to die, and then suddenly jumps up and tries to kill a poor, hard-working veterinarian."

"I don't know what got into him last night," said the sergeant. "He *never* did a thing like that before."

"No?" I jeered. "I'll bet he's a regular ladies' pet, and that's why a horse of his size is not in a lead-team where he belongs. I guess he weighs eleven hundred pounds if he weighs an ounce. What's he doing as a single-mount anyway?"

"Well," said the section-chief weakly, "he never was rightly broke to harness, and he *is* a little hard to handle sometimes, but I tell you he's a mighty good all-'round horse."

"He sure looks like it," I sneered, "rolling-eyed, Roman-nosed, cat-hammed, and hammer-headed. He looks ugly, he acts ugly, and I think he *is* ugly. But he comes from my home country, and I guess I can ride him. He'll make a good souvenir because he'll remind me of Central Oregon."

All this time I noted that the *F*-Battery sergeant had been sneaking furtive glances at my beautiful, black single-mount, standing at my elbow, a picture of aristocratic amiability. I rubbed the animal's shoulder appreciatively, and he reciprocated by nosing my cheek.

"There's a horse," I said, "that hasn't got a mean hair in his hide. Talk about a single-mount! Riding that horse is like sitting in a rocking chair. Look at him. He is about the handsomest horse in this regiment, maybe in this brigade. And he knows his duty, too. He wouldn't dream of dogging it on the march and lying down under full pack, much less of kicking a commissioned officer in the belly. He wouldn't kick anybody. He wouldn't hurt a baby. He *would* make a ladies' pet. *There* is a lovable horse."

"What's wrong with him?" demanded the section chief.

"Nothing," I said, "Absolutely and unqualifiedly nothing. Nothing of consequence."

"Yeah?" said the *F*-Battery man. "That's why you are not only willing but anxious to trade him for that damn' buckskin? Now let's be formal, Sergeant Peddiwell, and honest. What is wrong with your single-mount?"

"He's from England," I said, "and naturally he has English manners and an English accent. While I am certainly not anti-English, at the same time I am pro-American in horses."

"Don't give me that guff," insisted the section chief. "What is the matter with that black horse?"

"He is not intellectually brilliant," I said. "I like to teach a horse tricks. He is a slow learner. Here, get on him and try him out."

The sergeant mounted Hunter, as I called the black horse, and he was of course captivated at once. The animal walked, trotted, and cantered around the field in his usual accommodating and agreeable fashion. Of course, the sergeant had no opportunity to try him out on a march.

That Hunter was the only Army horse I ever knew who was too stupid to stay in a column and follow the animal or vehicle ahead of him. He had to be guided or led all the time. He knew no spoken, visual, or bugle commands or signals. At *halt,* you had to pull him up. At *forward, march,* you had to touch him with your spurs. You had everlastingly to keep those bridle reins in hand, or he would bump into the muzzle of a field-piece or wander out to one side into the path of a motorcycle-dispatch rider, an ambulance train, or the passing files of infantry. A blind horse of modest mental endowment could have done better. There was nothing wrong with Hunter's eyes. He had 20-20 vision. It was merely his intelligence quotient that was lacking.

We made the trade, checking with our battery commanders and stable sergeants. I led Toot Sweet to our picket line, took my saddle off Hunter, and then watched the happy *F*-Battery man ride away with his beautiful new single-mount.

Before I rode the buckskin, I groomed him carefully, examined his feet, and talked to him confidentially. He gave me a hard eye but attempted no aggression. In the almost two years that I knew him, he sometimes nipped at soldiers, particularly infantry-men, and he was never a safe horse for a stranger to approach from the rear, but he never bit or kicked at me. He struck me once when I was sleeping in front of him in a French boxcar, but I believe that this was the result of an understandable misunderstanding.

It was in March, 1918, when the German High Command struck suddenly with about one hundred divisions in column at the junction of the French and British Armies on the Western Front. Marshal Ferdinand Foch, the Allied commander-in-chief, had just organized his Army of Maneuver. He rushed it by road and train to the point of the German breakthrough.

Toot Sweet and I, as submicroscopic parts of this action, learned what a forced march in the field artillery was like. This, I believe, is where the term *hell-on-wheels* originated. We walked and trotted in alternate quarter hours for sixty minutes. Then we halted for ten minutes with the exhausted cannoneers sleeping where they fell, the fatigue-drugged drivers loosening cinches and rubbing their horses' trembling legs, and the battery commanders and buglers staring at their watches as though they hated them. Then *stand to horse* was sounded, the corporal gunners slapped the cannoneers awake, *prepare to mount, mount,* and *forward, march* followed inexorably, the caisson wheels rolled again, and the whips rose and fell. Occasionally a horse or mule went down and could not regain his feet. A pistol barked, harness was dragged from the still, warm body, a spare animal was trotted forward and put into the team, and the cruel cycle of walk-trot, spur-whip was maintained.

It was during this march, about the middle of it, in fact, that our regiment reached a railroad and boarded trains. Toot Sweet, seven other horses, my caisson corporal, and I shared one of the toy boxcars which made *40 hommes ou 8 chevaux* a well-worn phrase. In the interest of strict accuracy it should have read ... *8 chevaux et 2 hommes* since two men traveled with each car of eight horses. Four horses were backed into one end of the car, another four into the opposite end, and the two men then slept crosswise under the horses' noses in the center of the car. This was a much sought-after berth and was one of the important perquisites of section chiefs, caisson corporals, and drivers. Sleeping with one other man and eight horses, with center doors open to the breeze, was highly preferable to being cooped up in the same space with thirty-nine men, of whom at least twenty-five would be convinced that fresh air was conducive to pneumonia.

When we boarded that train, neither men nor horses had eaten for the last sixteen hours of rapid marching on heavy roads. We hoped to draw emergency rations of oats in four or five hours. In the meantime each man was ordered to break open and eat one package of hardtack from the emergency rations in his pack. The drivers and other mounted men generally shared this hardtack with their horses.

I gave Toot Sweet precisely half of my ration, counting the crackers so that there could be no suspicion of even unconscious favoritism. He wolfed his portion greedily and then pawed, asking for more, while I tried to eat my hardtack in a civilized manner. I told him that he would get oats in a few hours—oats which he would not have to share with me. He kept pawing arrogantly. Finally, after finishing my dinner, I slapped his knees with my open hand and gave him a direct order to stop that pawing. I advised him to go to sleep and forget his belly. Then I lay down to go to sleep myself.

Toot Sweet, not being permitted to paw any more, was now blowing his nose scornfully. I did not wish to curtail that small liberty, so I put my steel helmet over my face to guard it from the discharge of equine nostrils. Then I fell asleep.

I was awakened by fiery comets in collision and blue and red stars wheeling through a white glare of space, and the helmet was jammed into my face. I attained full consciousness as I felt that heavy horseshoe scrape by my ear. Toot Sweet had struck me on the helmet.

I struck him with a trace chain for this offense and told him that if he were my property instead of that of the United States of America I would be gravely tempted to put a .45-caliber bullet between his eyes. He understood the intent of my remarks well enough but showed no remorse, staring at the candle I had lighted and snorting in an unpatriotic manner. He seemed to imply that he regarded himself as no one's property, and that if he ever got through the war alive he would never love the United States again or any other damned country.

I wish now, after these many years, that I had not hit Toot Sweet that night with a trace chain. I can see now why he struck me. He thought I could pull hardtack from my saddle pockets at will. He probably knew I could not produce oats and hay that way. He had seen me draw them from the supply dumps. But hardtack was another thing. I was keeping him on short rations out of pure cussedness. He knew, furthermore, that I had my helmet over my face. He thought, *I'll just tap that no-good so-and-so to keep him awake,* and as he reached out to do this, the French engine-driver slapped on the brakes and unbalanced the horse. If you weighed 1,100 pounds, you would find that a suddenly decelerating train, when you were standing on three legs, would make you unsteady. The train lurched, and that big, winter horseshoe dragged Toot Sweet's foot down a little faster than he had intended. I can imagine him thinking, *If I had really put my weight behind that tap, Mr. Hardtack Hoarder would never have got that helmet off his face alone.*

I suppose that this long explanation of Toot Sweet's conduct merely reflects the grief I feel when I recall practically any punishment I ever gave any animal, man, or child—particularly any child.

I am not attempting to give the history of any of these military actions. I will merely say in connection with this incident that the horses got their oats at three o'clock the next morning, the men had coffee with their hardtack at the same hour, and by four we were off the train and on the road again with a new crack at the walk-trot-whip-spur routine. The Army of Maneuver arrived in time—time bought for it mainly by one Cockney division that died in its position almost to the last handful of men. At the end, that handful got up out of its holes with empty bandoliers, fixed bayonets, and *attacked*. I am proud to have fought, however unimportantly, in the same quarrel past the bodies of those very gallant men.

As the spring days lengthened and the spring marches and fights wore on, Toot Sweet and I came a little closer to mutual appreciation. He still gave me a hard eye in the mornings and occasionally bucked a few jumps when I mounted and allowed him a little head-play. This gave the men, especially the plodding cannoneers, a moment of relaxation as they shouted, "Ride him, Cowboy." They regarded the pair of us as their Wild-West performers.

One day my Western tricks put me into the gravel at an awkward moment. The battery was going through an intersection that was being shelled in desultory fashion by German 150-millimeter howitzers. I waited until I thought I sensed a lull in the enemy fire, and then I started my section past the danger spot at a fast trot, hoping to get everything clear before the next shell landed.

Toot Sweet and I were swinging along just ahead of the gun-team's leaders. It had begun to rain, and a cannoneer riding the caisson ahead of us started to put on his slicker. The wind caught it from his hands and dropped it in the road in front of Toot Sweet. I leaned down quickly to pick it up. My right hand was gripping the McClellan saddle pommel, and my left hand had just grasped the slicker when the government-issue cinch buckle broke. I went on my head in the muddy road, with saddle, pack, and scabbarded rifle crashing down between my legs.

The lead horses of the gun-team jumped to the right to avoid stepping on me, and the swing and wheel horses followed them. I heard a brake start to squeal and, worried by the thought that the gun might be halted in the intersection, I signaled *trot* vigorously and waved the column forward from my reclining position. Then I stood up to collect my scattered equipment. As I did so, I bumped into the big buckskin. He was standing practically over me. He was looking at me with what I imagined was mild concern tinged with contempt. "What the hell are you doing down there?" he seemed to be asking.

I threw the saddle back on the horse and held it in place as I ran beside him until we were out of the intersection. As I made a swift repair of the cinch, I thanked the horse. "You, Mr. Sweet," I said politely, "are a real *cheval de guerre.*" He rolled his eyes to signify that he understood French, but he seemed interested mainly in watching a howitzer shell explode in the intersection.

At the next halt, Jack Murphy, lead driver on the gun, spoke admiringly of Toot Sweet's performance. "That big horse," he said, "has got a hell of a lot more between his ears than just bone to keep a bridle on."

"How do you figure that?" I asked.

"Why, what I mean is," said Jack, "that buckskin was trottin' fast when you went off. I'll bet he was takin' ten-foot steps. When the cinch popped and you hit the ground, he went up on his hind legs right now, swung left like a polo pony, and brought his front feet down plumb next to you. Any other horse in this regiment would have trotted right on with the column. The reason he didn't, by God, is because he *thinks.* He figures he's your single-mount, and when you suddenly dive off and slide along the ground, he stops to check up on you—and also keep somebody from accidentally walkin' on you."

I laughed and said, "You may be right, Jack." Then I noticed that Toot Sweet was eyeing us, for all the world as though he were listening to our conversation. In a sudden burst of affection, I reached over to pat his neck. He laid his ears back at the caress to show that he was tough and immune to flattery.

Then came May and an enemy drive down the Château-Thierry road to Paris, and suddenly here was the most spectacular day Toot Sweet and I had spent together. We stood at the edge of a wood with batteries behind us while our battalion commander wondered whether, when the guns were emplaced behind a row of small trees across the wheat field before us, the shells would clear the trees. In a moment the horse and I were crossing the field to find out. I carried a little device for measuring angles of fire, and Toot Sweet furnished fast transportation.

When the nearest German artillery observer saw the horse and me, it was obvious to him that we meant field guns coming out of the woods very shortly, and he turned a battery of 77-millimeter weapons on us. We went across the field so fast, however, that the shells were consistently over us. When we reached the line of trees I dismounted on the run. Then I trotted along, measuring the angles every ten yards. I paid no further attention to my horse, assuming that he would join the battery. Since the guns were going into action here, I had no further use for a mount.

As I turned to signal the battalion commander that our line of fire would clear the trees, I bumped into Toot Sweet's nose. My drivers later told me that as I ran along that line of trees, the horse followed me like a dog. Jack Murphy added that whenever I stopped to measure an angle, the horse looked up at the tops of the trees. "He knew what you were doin'," Jack insisted, "and he was checkin' up on you to make sure you didn't misread that dingus."

The batteries came across the field into action front at the gallop.

I have gone into action with infantry, and with a good, professional outfit, it is a stirring sight. To see the expert riflemen tossing sand into the air to get the correct windage, to watch a platoon fan out precisely to cover a rushing squad, to hear a quiet-voiced company commander say as though inviting you to have a glass of milk, "Will you take those people out at eleven o'clock?" —all these and many other details like them mark the elegance of the polished foot-soldier.

I have seen other arms in action too. I saw the great Spahi cavalry charge at Soissons on July 18, 1918. In World War II I saw modern armor in action more than once. I rode on war-planes making their bombing runs, and once, from a reconnaissance plane, I saw United States ships meeting attacks from enemy aircraft as they steamed swiftly against opposing cruisers and destroyers. These are all exciting events and tend to race the participants' or observers' blood.

But, to me, for sheer drama, nothing in the way of military action will ever quite equal the spectacle of old-fashioned field-artillery going into action at a gallop under fire. The guns and caissons come forward as though they are going to over-run the position, and then a bugle sounds sharply, a whistle shrills, or a studious-looking officer with thick-lensed spectacles stands up in his stirrups and swings an arm. The lead-teams jump to the left. The swing and wheel-teams follow through the arc. The linch pins are jerked. The trails hit the ground with spades digging in. The cannoneers swarm aboard the guns on the run, the black muzzles peer skyward, a section chief raises his hand and then suddenly drops it, the first gun barks and sits back in recoil, and a young voice calls triumphantly, "First round on the way!" Now the whole line is ablaze, as the drivers trot back out of range, and recruit horses stand on their hind legs in horror at the noise of their first time under fire.

On this particular day, however, I gave the oncoming batteries only cursory attention. I was interested mainly in studying that big buckskin horse. He held his head high and with ears forward watched each German shell break. Occasionally he glanced at me in obvious inquiry.

Probably I knew what was going on here. He was trying to understand it. It was interesting and part of our job.

If I had been alone, I would have hit the ground when those shells broke nearby. As it was, I stood up proudly beside that proud horse. For the first time, he looked handsome to me. As the battery reached our position, I pulled his head against my chest for a moment and said, "You, Mr. Speedy, are a *sunka wakan.*" He kept his ears forward and rolled his eyes a little. As Jack Murphy led him away, I watched him for a moment before I turned to the gun.

After the angle-measuring incident along the line of trees beyond the wheat field, the general social milieu began to have a noticeably behavior-changing effect on Toot Sweet. Now, for example, when he bucked a little in the mornings, the performance seemed to be a trifle more studied and formal than it had been previously. He was doing it in part for the sake of his audience. He was definitely more conscious of the audience's reaction. When I would pat him and felicitate him sometimes, saying, "You just about dumped me on that first jump, Toot," or, "You're getting to be a real outlaw, *Monsieur Suite*," he did not lay his ears back any more but appeared to be taking all compliments in graceful stride.

Soon afterward, when the horse got his first wound, a cut in the shoulder from an almost-spent rifle bullet, he permitted even strangers to come up and admire the gold wound stripe on the forward off corner of his saddle blanket, without offering to bite them. He knew that an old soldier must learn not to be irritated by personal relationships that might well annoy a recruit.

It was when Toot received his second wound, and I my first one, however, that he came fully into the military limelight. This was in October, 1918. I was now a first lieutenant. One of my duties in a particular sequence of fights was to ride back, hunt up batteries that had gone astray or had otherwise been delayed, and guide them to their positions on the front. Since time, of course, was breathing down our necks, as it always is in battle, I rode back to the missing unit as fast as possible. My mount then got a measure of relief as we came up with the battery to the lines at ordinary forced-march speed.

I usually changed horses on each trip, except when it was Toot Sweet's turn. I employed him for two trips. This was both in compliment to him to show him how high he ranked and also a matter of expediency. He could travel twice as far as the average single-mount, do the job faster when we were going back for a battery, and end his double stint still able if necessary to run a rapid two or three miles.

One morning about two o'clock, I looked for a roan horse whose turn it was to carry me, I thought. Through some oversight of a caisson corporal or stable sentry, the horse was not on hand. In my hurry, I decided to take Toot Sweet again, although he had enjoyed only about four hours' rest since I had ridden him on a previous combination of two trips. This casual decision was personally one of the most important that I made in that war, perhaps in any war. I checked to see that the buckskin had been properly groomed and fed, put his blanket carefully on his back, added my new, light-weight, French saddle, and then swung my rather tired frame aboard. For more than sixty hours my own sleep had been only in that saddle when bringing batteries forward. It was broken into those very short sequences between the moment I lost consciousness and the time I regained it a few seconds later, hanging by my left wrist with face alongside a stirrup. The wrist tied to the pommel was our customary safety measure in those days.

This trip started quietly but soon became unusual, as though in forewarning of its spectacular end. The night was cloudy and dark. A cold wind whipped the trees along the road. Toot Sweet was in a deliberate gallop as we met a regiment of 75-millimeter guns going forward. Ordinarily I kept him down to his swinging trot as the best gait for speed and endurance in the long haul, but sometimes he wanted to gallop a little to warm us up. This was one of the times.

I do not know how both of us failed to see or hear that ambulance. Of course, it was not lighted. The road was under enemy observation, and no lights were allowed. There was only one man, the driver, in the vehicle, and he may have been partly asleep, a hazardous state to be in while passing to the left of a horse-drawn column. The wind was against Toot's tail and therefore carrying our sounds away from us. The hooves, wheels, and trace chains of the passing artillery made some noise. It seemed strange, however, that neither the horse nor I heard the cough of that Ford engine before the collision.

I think Toot Sweet turned a complete somersault. Certainly he landed on his back, judging from the mud and gravel I found wedged in the seat of the saddle. I do not know what acrobatics I performed, but fortunately I had not yet engaged my wrist in a shawl strap and, as is ordinarily the case in such emergencies with one who has ridden horses since childhood, I cleared the saddle automatically and fell away from my mount. By the time I reached him, he was on his feet, heading back in the direction from which he had come, and snorting derision at the creature we had hit.

As the ambulance driver came running back to determine how badly we were maimed, I was examining Toot Sweet's legs and body with my hands and could find slight sign of injury. Actually he received only one small abrasion on his neck from the collision. My physical memento of the occasion was a somewhat battered left knee which had helped Toot Sweet's shoulder demolish the top of the ambulance.

Granting that ambulance bodies in 1917–18 were made of rather light metal, one had still to admit that the vehicle came out rather surprisingly second-best in its encounter with an Ochoco Valley horse. I think that the left front fender of the ambulance tripped Toot Sweet at the moment in his gallop when all four feet were off the ground. He hit the top of the ambulance with his near shoulder. I assisted him a little by demolishing the left light-bracket with my knee, and the job was done. The ambulance had to turn around and head for a repair dump. The horse and I went on about our guidance business.

Without further incident, we found the battery we were to guide. Just as dawn broke we brought it up to its position and watched it go into action. Then we turned and started toward our own battery's horse lines.

There was some enemy shelling along the road we were traveling, but hardly enough to be especially noted by either of us. A half-million American troops were being swung up in preparation for a final assault, and the Imperial German forces were striking back here and there in delaying actions, but Toot and I were more interested in oats, coffee, and sleep than in tactical or strategic musings.

We were passing through a cut in the road, close enough to our battery's picket line to be almost but not quite in sight. I had now slipped my wrist from its shawl-strap security, and the horse had lengthened his stride in anticipation. Then the shell struck. It came from a 150-millimeter howitzer and was fused to break on contact. It hit the top of the cut to our left. One substantial fragment took me in the left shoulder, and another knifed the horse's near foreleg just above the knee.

The explosion knocked me out of the saddle and collapsed both sides of the cut to some degree. On the side where I fell, it was enough to bury me under about a half-ton of wet sand. I went down with my face against my right forearm, a circumstance which perhaps kept me from almost immediate suffocation. The damp cloth of the jacket arm acted as a filter.

I was unaware of all this at the time, however, because the concussion had not only knocked me off my horse but had also knocked me out. I remember hearing the shell whistle. I remember leaning forward along Toot Sweet's neck. The next thing I remember was seeing Robert E. L. Woods' anxious face.

He and Jack Murphy at the picket line had heard the shell land and had glanced idly in that direction. They saw Toot Sweet gallop riderless into view around the corner, stand up on his hind legs, and then gallop back into the cut again. When they rode up bareback on the nearest mounts they could grab, they found the buckskin pawing madly to get me out of the sand. I think he might have done it alone, too, at that.

"I swear he was cryin' as he pawed," insisted Jack Murphy, but one must make allowances here for Celtic blood.

Perhaps the Peddiwells have some Celtic blood. I know that I got to my feet after first-aid bandages had been put on Toot Sweet and me, examined his bandage critically, and then, in the manner of a French general bestowing a *croix de guerre,* kissed him twice, once on each cheek. He did not flinch from this ordeal but merely regarded me thoughtfully.

I know that many people who were acquainted with Toot Sweet and me in the Army of Occupation in Germany think that I taught him his distinctive method of responding to the command, *eyes right,* at a formal review, but they are wrong. The gesture was his *wakan* to him alone as Holly Woman would have said, and I think it came definitely from his having two wound stripes. A number of soldiers had two wound stripes, and I recall one member of the regiment who had three, but Toot Sweet was the only horse in the brigade with two. He was also one of the few buckskins in the American Expeditionary Force. In addition, now, he had a desire for uniqueness in a dignified manner. It was no longer necessary or possible for him to distinguish himself by cheap aggression.

Thus it came about that the animal who had started as a malingering, kicking recruit could end less than two years later as a reliable but colorful veteran.

I never knew completely how famous Toot Sweet was until I reported one evening early in World War II for duty on a certain Pacific island. I had hardly dismounted from the troop-carrier airplane when an orderly said in old-fashioned phraseology that surprised me, "Sir, the commanding general's compliments, and he desires you to report to him at your earliest convenience." I hurried to my new commander's quarters, wondering what duty he had in mind for me. I had never seen this major-general before, I thought, but he greeted me warmly with an outstretched hand and a sack of Bull Durham.

"You don't know me," he said, "but I sure as hell know you. I was a second lieutenant of infantry in that division. We would pass in review on the Heights of Vallendar above the Rhine, do a column left, and come around to halt alongside the band which was opposite the reviewing stand. Next the brigade of artillery would come past the stand, regiment by regiment, with wheels rumbling and trace chains jingling, and finally there he would be, walking in front of a battery, a big, Roman-nosed buckskin horse, ridden by a wild-eyed kid of a first lieutenant with his left arm in a sling. The kid would sing out, *Eyes right,* and then that horse would stand almost straight up on his hind legs as his rider saluted, drop down as easy as if he was walking on cushions, take a couple of steps, and stand straight up again. Then the lieutenant would give the command, *Front,* and the horse would drop back to a sedate walk, look over at the infantry, and sneer—the only horse I ever saw that actually sneered."

"He didn't mean it that way, General," I said. "He liked soldiers, even dough-feet. He wasn't sneering. He was just laying back his ears a little to answer those birds who always hailed him when they were still supposed to be at attention."

"I know," laughed the general. "They would say, 'Toot Sweet, you old so-and-so, how are you? Swing around a little so we can see your wound stripes.'"

Toot Sweet died peacefully on a Rhineland farm in 1925. The general who remembered him so well has been dead since the taking of Okinawa. I think the boy who rode him has also largely ceased to exist since the fall of 1919.

Although Sky Bow was an infantryman in my division, I seldom saw him. He picked up two machine-gun bullets in his left leg during the March, 1918, fight. I did not know he was wounded until he was back in a base hospital. He returned to his regiment in time to take part in the June engagements.

On July 2 I was sent forward with an instrument detail and found myself lying alongside Sky Bow's battalion. In a lull at dusk that evening, I sought him out. He was sitting in a shallow trench, staring at the German lines.

I greeted Sky Bow in English. He turned and, without a flicker of expression on his face, answered me in Lacotah. I fell hesitantly into the old, boyhood language. He showed me four *Gott–mit–uns* buttons, cut from the blouses of German soldiers whom he had successfully encountered in close combat.

"Four is the *wakan* number," he mused.

"Waugh!" I said approvingly. "Scalps?"

"No, my friend," he replied gravely, "these are merely coup-sticks, or maybe they are coup-feathers. They are not scalps." He glanced at my helmet as though looking for an insigne of grade, which I was not wearing. Then he continued, "White soldiers do not take scalps. White officers would not like it, and we are pale-eyed, are we not?"

His manner was more Indian than it had ever been when we

were children together, but it was not bitter. I felt in some manner nearer to the man than I had to the boy. I took a long-hoarded bar of chocolate from my musette bag, raised it in the plains gesture of giving, and said, "For my almost-brother."

He accepted the gift graciously, a slight ripple of amusement lighting the depths of his eyes. "It should be a horse," I added apologetically, "but it would be hard to ride one into those fast-speaking guns."

Sky Bow laughed in relaxed fashion. "We could eat him," he said, "and most of the time in this war party I have been hungry enough to eat at least half a horse. But I will eat this instead"— he patted the chocolate bar—"and I will remember that we two are sons of Sunka Wakan Wakan, striking coups for him."

"For him," I said, "for Holly Woman, and for all the rest of them."

Sky Bow laughed again, this time, I think, a little cynically. Somewhat later, we exchanged the old plains salute, and I crawled back to my detail.

This was my last conversation with Sky Bow, but I saw him once more on July 4 in the assault on Vaux. He and his corporal were at the point of their company's advance. As they took a machine-gun out of action with grenades and bayonets, another machine-gun down the street picked them both off.

I am proud to say that I had not so far regressed into the pale-eyed culture that I could not compose and chant a death-song for my almost-brother. It ran:

> Sky Bow died here today,
> Striking coups for his people:
> Vaux is the name of this town;
> Vaux is a good place to die!

I repeated the last line, almost unconsciously, each time I fired that day at a German soldier. I had a star-gauge Springfield, and I was dusting off machine-gunners with it. Finally one of my wing-men asked me curiously, "What language is that you're talkin', Chief?"

"Never mind my language," I snarled. "Just attend to your own knitting!"

I was astonished at the intensity of my reaction, and I was ashamed of it a little later when I overheard the instrument sergeant explaining indulgently, "His Indian buddy was killed up there by the railroad depot this morning."

When I got back to my saddle-bags a few days later, I wrote to the agent on the reservation in Montana and enclosed a picture letter for Medicine Horse and Holly Woman. I showed Vaux and the railway station. I pictured Sky Bow and his war-party chief in action against the machine-guns. I drew the six batteries of howitzers under the skyline and the field telephone wires that related me to them. I even tried to picture the death song. I never attained much skill with a pencil, but I suppose I came closer to it that day than ever before or since.

When my letter arrived, as Holly Woman told me on my visit to her in 1920, the Chief shot his best horse for Sky Bow to ride in the Shadow Land.

"It was a great sorrow for him and for you, my Almost-Mother," I said.

"A proud sorrow," she remarked calmly, holding up her hands to show the stumps of the little fingers she had cut off in double mourning. Medicine Horse had died of influenza three months after his grandson was killed.

"It is a proud thing," said Holly Woman, "to have been the wife and the mother of such men."

I saw Jim only once during the war, soon after his infantry regiment had landed in France. It was the day before the Battle of Saint Mihiel opened, and I was busy helping to get batteries up to the line of departure in time for the next morning's zero hour. I had time only for a quick handshake and passing of good wishes to the boy. I had not seen him for four years. He looked, talked, and acted more like Mr. Webster than ever. Only that

Collingwood nose reminded you of his mother, and perhaps that added to his good looks. He was certainly handsome in a spick-and-span uniform that had not yet seen very much marching, let alone action.

I never had to write a letter of bad news to Mr. Webster, for Jim went through Saint Mihiel and the later Meuse-Argonne offensive without a scratch. He was discharged in the grade of captain at the age of twenty-three. He had enough of his father in him so that he was never conscious of his own rank or of yours. He was in the National Army and thus got back into civil life in March, 1919. He married a girl who had been his classmate at the state university. Mr. Webster sent him to Juniper Wells to act as manager of the Bar-W and the other family enterprises in Montana.

Since I was in the Regular Army and was assigned to the occupation forces in Germany, I did not get back to the United States until later in 1919. I resigned my commission in September of that year.

I rode trains until I finally reached Bend, Oregon. There I caught a ride with the star-route mail carrier who served the Ochoco region.

The mail box at the Jay-Jay is about a half-mile from the ranch house. As we came up the road from the Crooked River bridge, the mail carrier indicated a horseman just starting away from the main stable.

"There's Mr. Webster now," he said. "He's comin' down to get the mail."

At my insistence, the carrier left me and my baggage at the gate by the mail box. He offered to drive me up to the house, but I told him that there were plenty of rigs available at Jay-Jay to get my equipment and that with much appreciation for the ride I refused to delay him further. He then gave me Mr. Webster's mail and drove his buckboard on down the road. I stood with the package of mail in my hands and watched the approaching horseman.

Mr. Webster was then in his seventy-fourth year, but he sat

as erect in the saddle as always. He was a good rider, but he did not have a horse-soldier's seat. He rode straight up, like a cattleman who had once been an infantryman and had never forgotten it.

On this day, as I watched the old gentleman, he came within a hundred yards of the gate behind which I was standing before he knew who I was. I was dressed in civilian clothes. The last time he had seen me I had been in uniform. Perhaps he had expected to see me in uniform again upon my return. He was now looking at me intently, trying to figure out my identity. At last his face suddenly brightened, and he recognized me. I emphasize this fact because I treasure it.

Mr. Webster smiled and raised his hand in the plains greeting. Then I dropped the mail, vaulted the gate, and started running toward him. I had seen his arm fall and his body slump forward over the saddle horn. At the same time, his big, bay mare began stepping daintily sidewise to keep him balanced.

I reached Mr. Webster and lifted him from the saddle. He did not speak. Probably he could not speak, but he knew I was there and gripped my hand firmly as I laid him on the grass beside the trail. Then I drew the pistol which he was wearing that day in a shoulder holster and fired it twice to summon help from the ranch house. He showed no sign of hearing the shots. I think he was already dead.

Mr. Webster was wearing a fine pair of handmade, flatheeled boots that he preferred. As I knelt by his body in shock, I remember staring at those boots and wondering for a moment whether he had any preferences about dying with them on. I dismissed the thought at once as somehow insulting to him. James Jonathan Webster was a man who had principles by which he lived. If you had asked him, I am sure he would have said dryly, "Die the way you have to die."

THIRTEEN

University
of Oskaloosa

I DO NOT REMEMBER spending any appreciable time or effort in deciding that I would go to a university at the end of the war and get my first degree as soon as possible. I had made the decision long ago, and Mr. Webster's death strengthened my resolution.

I was well aware of the prestige which teaching enjoyed in Mr. Webster's estimation and of his own desire to have been a member of that profession. I wanted to be a teacher myself, and Mr. Webster's views supported my own motives. Undoubtedly such other influences as those of Medicine Horse, Henry Liberty Brown, and William Preston MacFarland also affected those motives.

Why did I go to the University of Oskaloosa? I suppose it was because Oskaloosa was as different from the University of the West as was any institution about which I had much information. The University of the West was a small, private, denominational, liberal-arts college. Oskaloosa was a large, land-grant university. West was ostensibly devoted to the formation of educated, Christian gentlemen. Oskaloosa had as its primary purposes the provision of advanced training and research services to the people of its state. Certainly, from the first, I was more in tune with Oskaloosa than I could ever have been with West.

I was twenty-six years old when I set myself the task of get-

ting a baccalaureate degree as rapidly as possible. Since I had
been expelled from the University of the West before finishing my
second semester there, I had only a half-year of college credit
with which to begin.

The University of Oskaloosa was on the quarter system. My
duties as executor of Mr. Webster's estate prevented my enrollment in the fall quarter of 1919. I had discovered the Correspondence-Study Department of the University Extension Division,
however, and I sought to make use of its offerings.

About the middle of October, 1919, I enrolled in a correspondence course in English History. There was a rule in the Correspondence-Study Department that a student could submit his
written lessons at the rate of one per week, unless he received *A's*
in which case he could turn them in as rapidly as he wished.

I engaged a room at the edge of the University campus,
about two blocks from the central library. Next I called on
Assistant Professor Charles H. Jasper, the faculty member listed
as instructor of the correspondence course in English History,
and asked him to let me read some of the *A* papers from any of
his courses.

Dr. Jasper was a nervous young man, probably about my own
age. He asked me why I wanted to see these papers. Ridiculous as
it seems in retrospect, I had the impression then that he was afraid
I might plagiarize something. I explained that time was pressing
on me, that I wanted to do eight or twelve hours of correspondence work before the winter quarter began in January, and that I
realized I must get marks of *A* to be allowed to work that fast. I
said that I just wanted to know what an *A* paper looked like.

This professor was an admirable young man, but he appeared to me to be easily flustered. I gathered that impression
from his brusque, over-businesslike manner. As I found out later,
he had been working on his doctorate during the war years, protected from the draft by a wife and two small children. It seemed
to me that this had been a fortunate circumstance both for higher
education and for the Armed Forces. I did not believe that he
could have gone through very much military training, much less

combat, and retained sufficient self-assurance to do graduate work afterward. His restrained manner and his obvious fear of the unaccustomed approach made me think that academically at least he was an ignorant provincial, yet I held this thought with some reserve. I knew that I could well be mistaken. I had been mistaken before in my judgment of men, young and old, and I was to be mistaken again more than once.

I remember a shy, timid-looking soldier whom I had under my command in the Rhineland, a rather slender boy of Italian descent from New York. His name was Giuseppe Coleocci. His buddies called him *Jew* in blatant disregard of the Catholic medal always hanging around his neck, but he never appeared to take offense at that sobriquet. "Most of my best friends are Italians," I heard him say once blandly, "but some of them are Jews, Protestants, or even Irish."

Our division disliked military police and had been so non-complaisant with that estimable organization that we were forced to do all our own provost and guard work. One evening, when I was commander of the guard, I walked into a beer-garden in Coblenz with Coleocci acting as one of my two wing-men. A big, fair-haired boy with a deep Georgia accent was seated at a table, sounding off to a couple of his comrades concerning the Negro problem. I heard him, out of the corner of my ear, as I walked along the bar greeting various acquaintances. Then to my horror, I heard Coleocci ask quietly, in his clipped New York accent, "If you don't like Niggers, what do you talk like one for?"

I turned just in time to see the big Georgian lunge across the table with a bellow and stop a flashing, straight left from Coleocci with his mouth before my other wing-man and I could interfere. I pulled Coleocci's belt and gun and put both him and the Georgian in arrest. I took them across the bridge of boats to the Ehren-breitstein side of the Rhine, where our regiment was quartered, but before we reached the guardhouse I stopped to give them some instruction.

"How far south have you ever been in the United States?" I asked Coleocci.

"I've been to Atlantic City, sir," he replied. "That's in Joisey," he added helpfully.

"Ah, yes," I said. "I believe I've heard of it, but somehow I thought it was near Coney Island."

"Oh, no, sir," Coleocci assured me earnestly. "It's a long ways from there; it's 'way down south on the Joisey coast."

"I see," I said. "Coleocci, you don't know enough about the South to put in your blasted eye. You are just an ignorant provincial."

Of the Georgia boy I next inquired, "Are you a pretty clever boxer?"

"Ah don't reckon Ah'm no expert, suh," he said sullenly.

"I don't reckon you are either from what I saw back there in the beer-garden," I commented. "You may or may not be interested in my opinion that this Private Coleocci whose left hand you ran your mouth into so easily is a very good boxer indeed. I have had some small training in that sport myself, and I know enough about it to realize that although I outweigh this man by thirty pounds he would probably cut me to ribbons in the first round. As far as fist-fighting is concerned and undoubtedly as far as Negroes are concerned, you too are nothing but an ignorant provincial."

"I'd have to do a lot of back-pedaling," offered Coleocci brightly, "because from what I hear the lieutenant has got a hypodermic in each hand."

"You're still in arrest, Coleocci," I said gloomily, "and I am nothing but an ignorant provincial myself with regard to boxing and a lot of other things. At least half the time I don't know whether I'm doing the correct thing, but right now if you two men want to shake hands, I'll forget this whole affair and release you from arrest."

Coleocci grinned amiably and stuck out his hand at once. The Southern boy responded a little more slowly but politely.

"Do you think you can remember that term, *ignorant provincial?*" I asked.

"Sure, I can remember it," said Coleocci. The Georgian only

stared woodenly. His honor had been injured, and he wanted to promise nothing.

"Maybe you don't understand what it means now," I said, "but if I have occasion to put either of you in arrest again I am going to see to it that you have adequate time to ponder its meaning in the guardhouse."

"I know what it means right now," said Coleocci cheerfully.

"Yes?" I inquired. "What does it mean?"

"An ignorant provincial," he explained, "is a local yokel who dopes out the whole damn' world from his own back-alley pitch."

Dr. Jasper's back alley was his department. First of all, he had to consult his department chairman. That gentleman sent him further to discuss the grave proposition with the director of the Correspondence-Study Department. On my fourth visit to Professor Jasper's office all the dangers had been properly weighed, I suppose, for I was finally allowed to read three papers for a correspondence course in Medieval History which Jasper stated were, in his opinion, efforts deserving marks of *A*.

I noted that all three papers were typewritten. One of them seemed to me to be somewhat unnecessarily wordy. Another had very involved sentences and single paragraphs filling almost a whole page. The third was more to the point and was copiously adorned with footnotes. I ventured the observation that the last paper was the best of the three. Jasper looked a trifle startled and then laughed modestly. "That one," he explained, "is my own. I write answers to each lesson myself to see what is involved."

I thanked him and thereafter kept away from his office.

I bought a typewriter and went to work. First, I read all the books assigned for the whole course. Then I read several other books which I thought might well have been listed also for the course. Next I wrote out the first four lessons by hand, putting in footnote references to all my readings, typed the lessons carefully and sent them to the Correspondence-Study Department. They came back in about a week with the required *A*'s on them, and by that time I had four more lessons ready to turn in. I believe that there were thirty-six lessons in that course. I finished them and took the final examination about December first.

I enrolled next in a course in Principles of Sociology, which I completed before the opening of the winter quarter. Then I signed up for a course in Elementary Norse, having some curiosity about how a foreign language could be taught by correspondence. So far as a reading knowledge of the language was concerned, it was taught to me very well. Of course, I had the advantage of having spoken the language a little when I was in the Danebod district, although I necessarily recited the verbs with a Danish accent.

I could not turn in my correspondence lessons while enrolled in a regular session at the University, but I could prepare them. I did so and turned them in during the spring vacation, took the final examination in Norse, and enrolled in another history course before the spring quarter began. I followed the same general tactics in the two-weeks period between the spring and summer quarters and in the five weeks' vacation at the end of the summer quarter.

By January, 1921, with four quarters of regular-session undergraduate study and six correspondence courses sandwiched between the regular terms, I was rated well into junior standing. In the winter, spring, and summer quarters of 1921, plus four more correspondence courses, I completed the requirements for the degree of bachelor of arts.

The correspondence work, in my opinion, was by far the most important part of my undergraduate training. Aside from the course in Norse, it was all in history, sociology, and English literature. I learned to write carefully, rapidly, and critically in these fields, after extensive readings in books and journals, a fair proportion of which, perhaps twenty per cent, I had selected myself.

I was twenty-eight years old when I completed the requirements for the baccalaureate in the summer of 1921. I thus had the advantage of considerably more maturity than the average undergraduate. I may have had also a better secondary education than most of my fellow students, particularly in the area of languages and sciences. I could read several foreign languages, and some of them, notably French and German, were useful in certain history and sociology topics.

It is my considered opinion that any industrious student of moderate ability and reasonable motivation could have done in two years all the work required for the A.B. degree at Oskaloosa in those days. The chances are that nobody could do it now the way I did it then for the simple reason that ignorant provincials on the faculty have probably long since changed the rules so that it is impossible for a student to turn in correspondence papers as fast as I did, no matter what the quality of his work may be.

One of the most firmly held superstitions in American academic lore is that four years in these ivied halls do something, *something,* for a boy or girl that cannot possibly be acquired properly in three years, or—most horrible to contemplate—two years. I use the terms *boy* and *girl* here advisedly, because this superstition is closely related to the delaying of adolescence, the endless nonsense of homecoming games, tugs of war, Junior proms, hell weeks, beauty queens, and all the other paraphernalia by which undergraduates are taught to be loafing dilettanti. Even in 1921 the dull stupidity of this creed was apparent; it seems incredible that more than forty years later it should still have followers, much less be countenanced by presumably adult legislators, regents, and alumni.

To return to my personal history, I can report that the class work I pursued in the regular quarters had a much slower tempo than did my correspondence work, but I enjoyed many of the courses in which I studied psychology, mathematics, chemistry, French literature, Spanish literature, philosophy, and education. Because I had been a rural-school teacher, I was not required to do student-teaching for my high-school teacher's certificate. Because I had been a soldier, I was exempted from the military-drill and physical-education requirements. Largely because I had learned in correspondence study to read both extensively and intensively, to write carefully organized and annotated papers, and to take detailed and comprehensive examinations, I received high marks.

Oskaloosa was experimenting with an honors system at that time. I took honors in educational psychology by giving individual intelligence tests to all fourth- and fifth-grade children, some two hundred of them, of a small city in the suburbs of the University's seat. I wrote an honors dissertation. This work had charts, graphs, diagrams, and tables showing intelligence distributions in those two grades. I confess that although I was interested in this project I did not regard it at the time as being much above the level of busy work. I do not regard it any more favorably now.

Later acquaintance with the history of the University of Oskaloosa revealed that the dean of the College of Arts and Sciences during my days as an undergraduate was an "honors" enthusiast and a dominant personality. He had wanted to attend Oxford University as a Rhodes scholar and had worked hard to be worthy of selection. The regional committee on selection, unfortunately, decided that more attention must be given to whole personalities rather than merely to scholars. They gave the appointment that year to a rugged young man with letters in football, swimming, and track whose highest marks were in music appreciation, oratory, and physical education. As a consequence, the dean hated those particular disciplines all the rest of his academic life. He did visit Oxford after he became a professor, however, and he was much impressed by the differences between a pass degree and an honors degree in that institution. Thus, in the spring of 1921, my honors adviser and I did obeisance to an Oxford tradition. I do not think it harmed either of us.

In speaking of honors, I am glad to report that I was elected to membership in Phi Beta Kappa. At the time this distinction was given to me, I did not regard it with sufficient awe. I thought it came automatically to anyone who received practically straight *A's*. My later researches in the history of Oskaloosa disabused me of that notion. I learned that when my name came before the society for election, it was opposed vigorously on two counts. First, the fact that I had been expelled from the University of the West was referred to in appropriately hushed tones. Second, the relatively large amount of credit I had received by correspondence study was scornfully cited.

It was on this occasion that Charles H. Jasper showed himself to be spiritually akin to Giuseppe Coleocci. In a voice trembling with indignation, as my reconnaissance agents later informed me, Dr. Jasper stated that my offenses at West were breaches of academic discipline and did not involve moral turpitude; that morality, for that matter, was not a proper standard for election to the Society of Phi Beta Kappa; and that the papers I had written for him in correspondence courses showed that I was capable of doing creditable work toward a master's degree, perhaps even the doctorate. His eloquence carried me just barely into the charmed circle of those who make philosophy the guide of life.

I learned in the Jasper case once more, therefore, to beware of first impressions. They are usually right, but when they are wrong they can be wrong as hell.

FOURTEEN

Superintendent of River Junction

I ENTERED educational administration in the fall of 1921. I had three important qualifications for such work. First, I was a university graduate with a high-school teacher's certificate. Second, I had been a teacher in a rural elementary school. Third, and most important of all, I had served in 1917–19 in the same battery of field artillery with Mr. Mulligan. By 1921 Mr. Mulligan was chairman of an Oregon school board which was looking for an administrator. The resultant appointment, and Mr. Mulligan himself, for that matter, could have occurred only in the United States of America and then only with ease in the Far West of that nation.

Mr. Mulligan's real name was Stanislaus Modjelewski. He was born a subject of the Russian czar. He emigrated from Poland to Pittsburgh in 1905 at the age of eighteen. In 1915, having saved his earnings as a steelworker, he removed to River Junction, Oregon. There he purchased an enterprise known as *Mulligan's Restaurant*. It will not be surprising to Oregon readers to learn that this institution was a Chinese eating house. Everybody who worked there, from the chief cook to the lowliest dishwasher, with the exception of Mulligan himself, was a Cantonese. Most of them, indeed, were named *Chen*.

In 1917–19, while the proprietor was serving in the Army, the senior Chen took over the Mulligan establishment and operated it efficiently and honestly. "As far as I'm concerned," I heard the proprietor once testify, "all Mulligans, Smiths, and Modjelewskis are crooks compared to them Chens."

I cannot say that I knew Mulligan Modjelewski very well during our service together in the Army except for one period of about twenty or thirty minutes. On that occasion, I was trotting through some French woods in company with a big second lieutenant of Polish descent. We were headed back to our battery kitchen for warm rations. We had just come from our guns which were engaged in a desultory duel with some enemy batteries. About seventy-five yards behind us, also headed for the kitchen, was Mulligan.

In our brigade training camp in the United States there had been at least one sharp altercation between this lieutenant and Mulligan. It was carried on in the Polish language, which none of the witnesses understood. Neither of the men involved ever volunteered an explanation of the quarrel, if that is what it was. At any rate, the private received a minor punishment of being confined to quarters for a few days for insubordinate language, a punishment which he did not appeal. My own knowledge of this situation was sketchy, as I was not well acquainted with either of the men. They belonged at that time to sections of the battery with which I had little contact.

On this chow-seeking occasion, a sharp-eyed German artillery observer spotted us as we crossed a small clearing in the woods and decided very properly to dust us off. He fired a salvo of four 77-millimeter guns in our direction. The lieutenant and I, as we heard the shells whining toward us, hit the ground, and I suppose Mulligan did likewise. None of us was scratched, but the little tree behind which the lieutenant had placed his head received a direct hit at its base on the opposite side from the lieutenant's cranium. The concussion knocked the young officer out. As I examined him, I heard another German salvo coming. I hit the ground again and pondered the obvious necessity of getting the lieutenant out of that area before one of the shells cut him up seriously.

I called to Mulligan as he came running along and explained the situation. "We'll have to carry him up to the top of that hill," I said, "to get him out of this fire."

"Let the son of a bitch carry himself," said Mulligan coolly.

I stared at the big cannoneer in astonishment. I had known other men who hated an officer, but this was the first case I had observed where the hatred included a willingness to let the officer get killed. I had to make a quick decision. I could give Mulligan a direct military order to help me carry the lieutenant, and disobedience of that order in the face of the enemy was a possible capital offense. Or I could handle the problem in a civilian administrative manner.

I chose the latter course. I got down alongside the unconscious lieutenant, a man who outweighed me by at least forty pounds and was now as limp as a wet rag, and began to work myself under him. As I did so, I cursed Mulligan loudly and fervently, casting reflections on his ancestry and courage. I even stated that I would be willing to waive my grade at some convenient later date for the pleasure of changing the geography of his repulsive features.

My decision proved to be the correct one. I had just staggered to my feet with the lieutenant across my shoulders when Mulligan came alongside, picked the burden off my back, and started running up the hill with it. He was an even bigger man than the lieutenant.

The officer regained consciousness on top of the hill as I poured a helmetful of water on his face. He thanked me for carrying him out of fire. I told him Mulligan had done it and had already gone for the stretcher bearers, but the lieutenant could not hear anything I said. Both his ear drums were broken.

The only time Mulligan ever mentioned this incident to me was on the night of September 15, 1921, just after he had signed my three-year contract as supervising principal of the schools of River Junction.

"There we are, Mrs. Appleyard and gentlemen," he said briskly to the clerk, the other two members of the board, and me. "We now got us a superintendent of schools, and I'll bet he's the first one in Oregon, anyway, who ever called the chairman of the board a son-of-a-bitchin', yellow-livered, Bohunk bastard *before* the contract was signed."

"How romantic," sighed the clerk. "Tell us all about it, Mr. Peddiwell."

"I know nothing of any such expressions, ma'am," I said, "and if any character ever used them anywhere to describe the chairman of this board he was lying in his teeth. For one thing, Mr. Mulligan is of Polish and not Bohemian descent."

In the next three years, these school-board members and their clerk were my chief instructors in the art of administration. From Mulligan I learned the administrative uses of an inquiring mind oriented toward progress. In all his waking hours, he was perpetually considering ways in which his restaurant, his town, his state, his country, and the school system over whose board he presided could be improved. Undoubtedly there were citizens in River Junction with higher intelligence quotients than Mulligan had; none used their abilities more singlemindedly for community betterment. I am convinced that even when Mulligan was considering the purchase of new table cloths for his restaurant, he had mainly in mind the goal of a newer and better River Junction rather than a bigger profit for Mulligan's Restaurant. I never had to labor a proposal for school improvement to him. If it was possible, he was in favor of trying it. He believed in testing plans in the fire of action.

Bill Turner, the second member of the board, was a steamboat captain on the Yukon River in the summer season and a cattle and wheat rancher about ten miles west of River Junction the rest of the year. He was a technician on boats, ranches, schools, towns, or anything else with which he had to deal. He wanted to know the details and how they meshed with one another before he would hazard a comment on some proposed new scheme. I learned from him to study the machinery of my organization with care and to figure out precisely how it would operate if I introduced a new procedure or gadget.

Jack Dumont, the third member, was the politician of the

board. From his position as station agent for an important railroad division point, he knew the railway officials and workers, the division superintendents and traffic managers, engineers, firemen, conductors, brakemen, switchmen, car inspectors, bridge carpenters, section foremen, and track laborers. He knew the ranchers as shippers of livestock and grain. He knew the business men as receivers of express and freight. Because he was a specialist in human relations, moreover, he made it a point to know everybody else. He was the only man in the community (besides me after I had been there a month), who knew the names of all the children of school age. He knew who was president of the Methodist Ladies Aid Society, and he had his hat off at ten paces whenever he met her on the street. He knew Mrs. Alka Gorwin also, the lady who ran a sporting house under the faint disguise of a hotel, and he took his hat off to her too. I learned from him that an administrator's chief coin is minted from individual human beings who, in a democracy, are always as good as the next person and must never be debased.

Mrs. Appleyard, under the Oregon law then prevailing for a district of River Junction's class, was clerk but not a member of the school board. She was actually the combined secretary and treasurer of the board. She was paid a yearly salary; I do not remember the amount, but it was quite small.

This woman was in many ways the most complex administrative personality in River Junction. In her official activities, she was scrupulously honest. She knew the law not only of school administration but also of public administration in general. Somewhat on the reverse of the medal, however, must be added the information that she was probably the chief bootlegger of that section of the country. I do not suggest that she ever carried any liquor herself. I doubt that she even drank it. But she took orders for it, gave the necessary directives for its delivery, collected payment for it, and arranged for its importation from Canada. The Federal prohibition agents never caught up with her. The local and county law-enforcement officers obviously had no desire to run afoul of her. She had powerful associates.

I liked Mrs. Appleyard. She was a widow of more than one husband, all living, I believe, and she was probably at least fifteen years my senior, but I always felt my soul warmed and my mind enriched by her presence. She never said anything banal except in mockery. She was not beautiful, but she wore a subtle air of wickedness that became her like a costly cloak.

Mrs. Appleyard taught me nothing of consequence except to watch all women carefully in any administrative or other situation. Perhaps that is an administrative precept or rule-of-thumb, though not important enough to be called a principle. For the information of my feminine readers, if any, I should add parenthetically that I never proposed marriage to Mrs. Appleyard. If I had done so, no doubt she would have refused the offer.

The River Junction Union School District had a total enrollment of somewhat less than 300 pupils in the eight elementary grades and the first three years of high school, all housed in one three-story, concrete building. There was one teacher for each elementary grade and four teachers for the high school. The latter unit had just been inaugurated the previous year. It had twelve children in the ninth grade, seven or eight in the tenth, and only two in the eleventh.

I taught two classes in the high school myself, one in American history and another in second-year Latin. Occasionally I substituted also for one of the elementary teachers.

My first administrative proposal was to raise the salaries of the teachers. I selected this item as a starter for three reasons. First, I had two high-school positions and one elementary place yet unfilled, and with the opening of school less than two weeks away, I needed attractive salaries to get the candidates I wanted. Second, the teachers who were already employed appeared from their records to be competent and well prepared. Third, I had a special device for raising salaries which I wished to test in practice.

I proposed that the monthly salaries be kept at their current levels, but that teachers be paid for twelve months rather than for just ten months of the year.

In presenting the proposal to the board, I first emphasized my belief that the raise would enable us to get and hold better teachers. This secured the chairman's support at once. Next, I explained that we would pay the teachers two months' salary instead of just one at the end of the school year, and another month's salary when they reported for work in September. This would enable the teachers to get through the summer period of travel or university study more smoothly than was customary. Teachers could not engage in summer work except with the board's approval; they were employed for the entire year. This description of the details of the system received Captain Turner's interested support.

Finally I pointed to the public-relations value of such an innovation. We would be the first district in our area to recognize in a formal salary-schedule that our teachers were engaged in education work twelve months in the year. The morale of our staff would be strengthened. We would become a marked district. Dumont saw at once the political values in this feature of the proposal.

Mrs. Appleyard's only contribution to the discussion was a cynical observation that it would be easier administratively to raise all salaries twenty per cent and continue to pay the teachers ten monthly salaries instead of twelve. The board received this suggestion coldly.

"We'd be no different from anybody else," complained Dumont.

"The teachers would all be broke as usual at the end of the summer," remarked Turner.

"It wouldn't give the same kind of real improvement," observed the chairman.

I employed the three new teachers from among those I had met at the University. The elementary replacement was an older woman who had previous experience in a one-room rural school. The two new high-school teachers were inexperienced but were both older than the usual college senior.

It would be difficult to exaggerate the cooperative attitude and high professional morale of the teachers in River Junction. I knew already the principle that the teacher makes the school, but I saw it demonstrated in that community with the clarity of a good laboratory exercise. We had only ten boys in the three high-school classes that first year, for example. I started giving a few lessons in wrestling with the notion that this was about the only sport in which we might produce a team. My Navy-veteran colleague thereupon said he had played a little basketball and offered to coach that sport. To my astonishment he produced a very creditable team the first year, using an empty lodge hall for a gymnasium. In the second and third years when he had a few more boys available, River Junction began to win games against larger schools, including Cut Bank, our natural rival.

Our science teacher, born in a European ghetto, working for years in New York City, and never living in a rural area until she came to River Junction, had her general-science pupils running Babcock tests for butter-fat on a few nesters' milk cows within a month after school started. What was most remarkable about this feat was that she had the warm respect of all the cattle ranchers and business men of the community as she did so. By Thanksgiving she had discovered a young rancher who had been a member of the state agricultural college's stock-judging team a few years earlier. She had him coaching a River Junction High School team within a week after she first saw him. To her simple and magnificent mind, stock-judging was scientific and therefore a proper topic of study in general science. She had me in her biology class telling the children about horses. She employed Captain Turner in the same course to describe the flora and fauna of the Yukon Valley.

When an elementary or secondary teacher in that school was ill for a day or two, we never employed a substitute. The other high-school teachers and I used our vacant periods, sometimes with elaborate shuffling of periods with elementary teachers, to step into the breach. It was instructive and often exciting to see how well a third-grade teacher could help the children with algebra in the high school while the Navy veteran taught eighth-grade arithmetic.

We were the most nonfragmented group of teachers that I have ever known. All of us were concerned to some degree with all the instruction of all the children. I suppose this would have been impossible if the system had been much larger. I know it would have been impossible with a group of ordinary teachers.

As an example of how these people operated, consider the case of little Charlie Turner, Captain Turner's younger son. He was in the third grade at the usual age of eight years. One day a high-school English teacher, who had taken the third grade for a period in an emergency, told me confidentially, "That little Charlie Turner can't read a lick. He just has a remarkable memory. He looks at the picture of the page of the reading book, and if he has ever heard that page read, he can recite the whole page letter perfect." I investigated this report and found it to be accurate. The regular third-grade teacher suspected something of the kind but had kept thinking that the child would finally begin to read some words.

I examined the child's eyes by various crude methods; they appeared to be normal. He could see and identify the most minute features of any picture. I consulted his older brother, or rather half-brother, a tenth-grader. This boy knew the answer but did not wish to appear disloyal to his step-mother, Charlie's mother. When I asked the boy whether Charlie ever read at home, however, the truth began to appear. "No," he said. "Mama reads all those little stories aloud to him. I never see him reading by himself."

Next, in my naive way, I appealed to Mrs. Turner. To my surprise she seemed offended when I suggested that she try the device of refusing to read to Charlie for a few weeks. "Of all things!" she said. "He loves to have me read to him. I'll do no such thing!" Then I appealed to Captain Turner himself, somewhat embarrassedly as may be imagined. I do not know, of course, what measures he took, but apparently he was master of his own household as well as of his steamboat. In about a month Charlie was reading to his mother and father in the evenings and in school was reading third-grade books he had never before seen.

In the second year of my term at River Junction we employed one additional teacher in the high school (which now had four grades) and three additional teachers in the elementary school. We rented temporary quarters, another lodge hall, for additional first-, second-, and third-grade classes.

The third year of my stay at River Junction we had a new elementary school building, housing the four lower grades. I became officially the superintendent of schools, since we now had enough pupils and teachers to qualify for the district classification required for my new title.

We had various other developments in the town. Among them were the River Junction Chamber of Commerce and the Pierced Nose Dam Association, of both of which I was executive secretary. We had the first woman mayor in that part of the world, Mrs. Appleyard. We had the River Junction Athletic Club, whose chief purpose was to beg, borrow, steal, hire, or cajole enough baseball talent to enable us to whip the town of Cut Bank, an inferior place which was unaccountably somewhat larger than River Junction. I was not secretary of the Athletic Club; I was president.

I had undoubted help in certain business and banking relationships by reason of my connection with the Webster enterprises. More important than these official relationships, however, were the personal advantages arising from the fact that I was a son of J. J. Webster. This circumstance was perhaps most pointedly emphasized in a difficulty I had in the spring of 1924 with the Ku Klux Klan.

This organization had been briefly revived in various parts of the United States in the post-World War I period. We had a unit in River Junction, I was told, but I did not know how many members it had, and I did not know any particular member. No one ever asked me to join the organization although I was white,

Protestant, and native-born, these being the three announced requirements for membership.

The Klan at that time was against Negroes, foreigners, Jews, and Catholics, and of course against all Un-American subversives, who were conceived to be especially plentiful in those four groups. I suppose the organization had some difficulty in our part of the country to find enough objects to make important opposition to them feasible. We had no Negroes, very few Jews, relatively few foreign-born citizens, and only a sprinkling of Catholics. It must have been especially difficult to be the Klan kleagle in River Junction. There was not a Negro family in the school district. There was only one Jewish merchant in town; he was native-born and an Army veteran. The nearest place of Catholic worship was a chapel in Cut Bank, thirty miles away. I suppose, although I had an academic interest in the problems caused by revival of the Klan, that it hardly occurred to me that I would ever have any dealings with that organization in River Junction.

I was therefore surprised one day to receive in my office an emissary of the Klan. I knew him by sight. He was a railroad worker. He had no children in the school; perhaps he was not married. He was somewhat larger than I and maybe ten or fifteen years older. I should have been warned by the quick feeling of prejudice I had against this man and watched myself accordingly, but I am a slow learner in many respects, and I confess sorrowfully that I had little inkling of what it now seems should have been clear to me at the outset of this affair.

The man said he was not a member but merely a messenger of the Klan. He then asked me how our teachers were appointed in River Junction. I explained that the superintendent of schools recommended people who in his opinion were qualified and the board then made the appointments or rejected them and asked for further recommendations.

"The Klan understands you got some Catholics and Jews teachin' in our school here," said the emissary.

"That is right," I said. "I know that some of the teachers belong to those faiths. We do not consider religion in employing teachers, however. We are concerned with education, experience, and personal qualities that equip the candidate for teaching. We do not ask what his religious views are." Actually we had only one Jew in the school system, the high-school science teacher whom I have already mentioned. There were three other teachers who were Catholics.

"The next thing we know you'll be appointin' Niggers to teach our children," the man said in what I regarded as a peculiarly offensive manner. To that moment I had been reserving judgment on his story that he was a messenger rather than a member of the Klan, but now I was suddenly convinced that he was not only a member but also probably an officer, perhaps the local kleagle himself. I am ashamed to remember that at this point I had a feeling of pride that I was keeping my temper well in hand and was talking in such a polite administrative manner.

As seems to be common in such cases where I am involved, however, the fool with whom I was dealing mistook my attempted courtesy for timidity, and when I began to explain patiently that I only recommended teachers to the board and that the board was the supreme policy-making body for the school district, the messenger-kleagle, or whatever he was, suddenly interrupted me with an arm-swinging gesture.

"Don't gimme that line," he snapped, "an' never mind tryin' to stall me neither. I want a straight answer!"

"I am trying to give you a straight answer," I said levelly, but I began to note that I had some difficulty of enunciation.

"Look, Junior," he said impressively, leaning across the desk, "git wise to yerself. This outfit kin play rough, an' it will play rough if . . ."

He did not finish his statement. The pride I had been feeling in my civilized, administrative manner was apparently of the kind that goeth before a fall, and my fall was abrupt. Before I was fully aware of what happened I had the man's shirt front wadded in my left hand and had struck him twice in the mouth with my right as I pulled him across the desk. I was so angry that

I was really saying nothing but only mumbling near-nonsense syl-
lables in a sing-song fashion, "rough-rough-rough! Too-rough-
bad!" It was the crunch of his front teeth breaking under the
second blow that brought me partly to my senses.

"Don't say anything," I advised him as quietly as I could,
"or I may kill you right now. Go on out and stay away from me
or I will kill you." As he walked out with his handkerchief over
his mouth, I remembered that he supposedly represented an organization, and my rage revived. "If you or your brother bastards
come back," I said, "You'd better have guns in your paws." He
made no reply.

I went at once to my room and took my father's .44-40 from
a trunk. I wiped the oil from it, loaded all six chambers, and put
it in the waistband of my trousers. Then I put a few extra cartridges in my coat pockets. I hesitated at the door of the room,
went back to the trunk, and took out my father's boot knife, but
I only rubbed it a couple of times reflectively, and then put it
back in the trunk.

By this time I was beginning to think more normally. I went
to Mulligan's Restaurant and reported the event to the chairman
of the board. It had occurred to me that if I did kill somebody or
got killed myself it would be well to have it officially known that
I was not just engaging in a private social misunderstanding.

It was now about ten o'clock in the morning. By six o'clock
that evening there were about a dozen, well-dressed, middle-aged
strangers in town. They wore their coats unbuttoned and did not
act like unarmed men. Shortly after I had noted them, Levi Kingman called on me. He wore his Sunday clothes and also had the
obvious bulge under his left arm. "Jest passin' through," he said.
"Gonna attend a Masonic meetin' here tonight. You still teachin'
school here, I guess?"

I took the old trooper to Mulligan's for dinner. When I
started to introduce the big Pole, the old man interrupted me
genially. "I know him already," he said. "He's a Mason too. Met
him at some of our doin's."

In that year, 1924, Levi Kingman was seventy-nine years

old. He was still manager of the Jay-Jay Ranch in the Ochoco. He showed no visible signs of mental or even marked physical decay. I do not know how fast or accurate he would still have been with a pistol, but I would have disliked having to match a draw with him.

As I watched Levi and Mulligan at dinner that spring evening I was at ease, but at the same time I was deeply disturbed. I listened to my friends' easy, relaxed conversation with one part of me. I even answered an occasional question and added a smiling remark or two of my own devising. At the same time another part of me sat in bitter judgment on J. Abner Peddiwell, school superintendent, who was talking to himself along these lines.

The Klan is a lawless organization. It relies upon violence and threats of violence to impose its will upon a community. It is a kind of secret mob.

And you, J. J. Webster's son—you are a model of nonviolence! You used violence this morning on a poor, ignorant man who had no slightest chance against you. You were not fighting for a principle; you were punishing an unlucky slob for affronting you personally. If he had resisted, you might have killed him. You were in the Army too long, Lieutenant, Sergeant—no, Corporal Peddiwell! That's the grade you really adorned!

But everybody seems to approve what I did this morning. *Everybody? Everybody can be just as wrong as anybody.*

FIFTEEN

Headmaster
of Crampton

"OUR JUDGMENT of men and parties," Lord Acton once observed, "is determined by the lowest point they touch." If this dictum is valid, and I think it is, the history of J. Abner Peddiwell, school administrator, should be examined with especial care for the spring of 1924. At that point an administrative career which had seemed flourishing only a year earlier was now sunk to its nadir.

It was my belief then that the administrator of a school system, working with changing instruments and materials to secure constantly shifting results, had a task of peculiar complexity. In the delicately balanced relationships among pupils, teachers, and the community, the introduction of a marked element of violence by the superintendent himself seemed unforgivable to me. The Klan incident, therefore, marked my lowest administrative point.

The Klan emissary lost his railroad job. He was not formally discharged, but, to use military phraseology, was merely run over the hill. No one told me the circumstances, and my own feeling of guilt kept me from inquiring about them; the indirect evidence, however, was clear. The man was hounded from the community. My sense of responsibility for his misfortune steadily deepened.

About a month later two unlucky young men from the Cut Bank klavern of the Klan started to burn a fiery cross one evening on the lawn in front of River Junction's main school building. They were apprehended by sheriff's deputies who were ostensibly forced to use blackjacks on them when they resisted arrest. Thereafter the Klan, if it continued to exist at all in that part of the state, must have gone underground.

At this juncture in my affairs and probably because of his understanding of my state of despair, William Preston MacFarland, the professor who had marked me permanently with the sign of the Gadarene swine, came to my aid. In April, 1924, he offered me a fellowship to work for my doctorate at the University of Oskaloosa where he was then dean of the School of Education. I went promptly to Mr. Mulligan, told him of the offer, and asked him to call a special meeting of the board to consider accepting my resignation.

Beyond a polite expression of regret, the big ex-artilleryman made few comments. He knew me well, and probably, with his keen concern for what would be best for the River Junction school system, he recognized that in my fourth year as superintendent I would not be as successful as I had been earlier.

Jack Dumont's warm commendations and expressions of friendship had some political overtones. As he shook hands with me I thought I could sense in him the quick formulation of new policies to fit the new personnel that would be needed in administrative ranks.

Captain Turner was more expansive than I had ever before observed him in a board meeting. He offered to help get me a superintendency in Southeastern Alaska. The Yukon country, he said, had no schools worthy of my experience, but places like Ketchikan, Sitka, and Juneau could use me. He knew the territorial commissioner of education, furthermore, he stated, and he could practically guarantee employment for me. He seemed disappointed to hear that I was going to Oskaloosa for further study. He did not say so, but no doubt it appeared obvious to him that what I needed was more practical experience. He did not see how I could get that by mooning around a university two thousand miles from Alaska. I think now that he was right, but then, in my youthful naïveté, I thought otherwise.

Mrs. Appleyard said nothing that I now remember. I recall only my disappointment at her strictly businesslike attitude toward the whole affair. If I had known then one-half as much about administration as I know now, I should have asked her to identify the point at which my administration had slipped. Had she performed this analysis, and had I been able to receive it intelligently, I might have learned enough about my capacities either to have become a great administrator or to have left the field of administration permanently. I may have feared that such analysis would merely re-enforce my feeling of professional incompetence.

When I gave the opening speech recently at the centennial celebration of River Junction's incorporation as a city, one of the older men on the present school board, identifying himself as Charlie Turner, said, "nothing was ever so colorful around here again as it was in 1921–24. The school board was composed of Dad, that Pole named Mulligan, and slick, old Jack Dumont. The mayor was Emma Appleyard, who looked like a Paris model and operated the bootlegging syndicate. The school superintendent already talked like a Ph. D., but he packed a .44-40 Colt in his waist band."

I kept a smiling countenance, I hope, but inside I remembered gravely the true circumstance of the ascent of the River Junction school system to the high rank it occupies today. It began when my ex-Navy colleague succeeded me in the superintendency and the Jewish teacher of science replaced him as principal of the high school. I was convinced then, as never before, that the end of my term as superintendent of River Junction was my administrative low point.

When I went to Oskaloosa in the summer quarter of 1924, I had only a thesis to write in order to finish the work for the master-of-arts degree. I had attended the university in the summer quarters of 1922 and 1923 and had thus acquired the necessary course credits in education and history. I had also collected materials for a dreary and nearly useless study of grade and subject costs in the high schools of the state. This thesis had no sparkle, no light, and little learning to relieve its dullness, but I immersed myself in it with enthusiasm.

This pleasant break, in which for hours at a time I could imagine that I was a scholar and forget that I had ever been an administrator, lasted less than two months. One morning, about August 1, Dean MacFarland called me into his office by a telephoned message which had been relayed through his secretary to my landlady the evening before while I was still working late hours in a library cubicle.

I entered the dean's office relaxed and smiling. I assumed that he was going to discuss the details of the labors I would perform as a graduate fellow beginning in the fall.

MacFarland's handsome face was unusually grave as he greeted me. "I hate to tell you this," he said, "because I know that you want to start working full-time on your doctorate in September, that you do not need a salary to put yourself through graduate school, and that you have no great hankering to be an administrator."

"What *is* the bad news?" I asked, trying unconsciously, I suppose, to present a proper executive mask.

MacFarland smiled. "I wouldn't say that it's necessarily bad," he said. "It is just that it may be temporarily disappointing. In the long run, however, it will be educational."

"Yes?" I said inquiringly. I thought I knew what the proposal and my answer to it would be. A small-town superintendency had become vacant suddenly because of someone's good or bad luck, and the dean had been asked to recommend a man for it. Everyone else who might be considered for such a job had a contract for the coming year by this time, and thus MacFarland did not have far to look. I was the only young superintendent available. I was mentally phrasing a polite refusal as the dean spoke further.

"You've heard of Crampton School?" he asked.

"Yes, sir, somewhat vaguely," I said. "It's a private day school, under a religious order perhaps?"

"Well, it's private all right, and it takes only day pupils, but it has no church connection," he answered. "How would you rate it?"

"I wouldn't," I said firmly. "I don't know enough about it even to begin rating it. Furthermore, I know nothing about private education."

"Yet you were graduated from Dr. Brown's school," said Mac-Farland.

"The Tum-a-Lum Academy," I said primly, "and while we are reciting my qualifications, permit me to state that I attended for almost a whole academic year a private college, The University of the West, as you may remember." I was feeling better now. It seemed very likely that MacFarland had been asked to survey the Crampton School, and he wanted me to help him.

At this point, however, he got ready to throw the grenade. "Heh, heh," he chuckled. "You have the right background. You were graduated from a private academy with honors and expelled from a private college with, if not exactly dishonors, at least—let us say—under a cloud, however filmy it may have been."

"Yeah, yeah," I agreed. It seemed ages since I had been nineteen. Twelve years is a long time to a boy of thirty-one. "What really raised hell with me were those Gadarene swine," I added.

He lifted his eyebrows a trifle—I suppose he had forgotten those hogs. Then he finally pulled the pin and tossed the grenade.

"I've beat around the bush or bushes long enough," he said. "We want you to take the headmastership of Crampton."

"Who are *we*?" I asked.

"The University of Oskaloosa," he said, "the School of Education, and I."

Only the third element in that trio carried any weight with me, but it carried enough so that I knew right then what my final answer was bound to be.

The dean detailed the situation which I summarize here. Crampton was a six-year secondary school, with grades VII to XII inclusive, situated on the former estate of the lumber baron after whom it was named and whose generosity had started the institution. It was housed in four rambling buildings. These were the Crampton family mansion of three stories and about twenty rooms; the former stable and carriage house, now used as a combined gymnasium-auditorium; a "guest-house" of ten rooms set to the rear of the mansion on the border of a five-acre lake; and the "junior" school with six classrooms and two offices. The first three buildings were of solid brick construction about forty years old. The fourth building, recently erected, was a frame structure of one story. It was comparable to the surplus-property buildings which were to become well known in the United States twenty years later.

Crampton had always possessed a reputation for scholarship, largely because its pupils were all headed for higher educational institutions and came from the propertied classes. Its reputation, from the beginning of the school in 1898, had generally far exceeded its quality, and never more than in the period 1919–24. Attendance had been steadily dropping during those last five years. The headmaster for that period, as he looked at the few applications for entrance and the numerous requests for transfers to the public junior and senior high schools for 1924–25, had suddenly tossed in his hand and resigned.

"Very interesting and quite sad," I commented when the dean reached this point, "and a good case for the chaplain with his crying towel. What has Oskaloosa and the School of Education to do with this case? Why not let the patient die and be replaced by sturdier institutions, public ones, preferably?"

"Well," said MacFarland, "Oskaloosa and the School of Education have been carrying Crampton in part because we are short of student-teaching facilities. Our own crowded University School has only the elementary grades I to VIII. We have been using Crampton for about fifty per cent of our high-school student teaching. It is located on the edge of our campus; students can walk to it in the ten-minute break between classes. We pay twelve Crampton teachers one-half their salaries and list them as instructors in the School of Education. I know this is not a good system, and perhaps in 1925–26, 1926–27, or later we may find another arrangement, but for 1924–25 we are stuck with it."

For a moment I was in the back row of MacFarland's class at the University of the West and he seemed to be asking, "What is the *lema,* the theme, of the Mexican Revolution?"

"All right," I said, *"Tierra y Libertad,* only for Crampton I guess it will be *Dinero y Carabinas,* or the like."

For a moment the old man (he was in his late forties) looked puzzled, and then he laughed sardonically. "Oh, sure," he said. "You're always thinking about some class long ago where you, I, or both of us said foolish things, but the simple truth is that I have persuaded the board at Crampton to offer you this job primarily because of the recommendation that Chairman Mulligan of the River Junction school board gave me over the telephone yesterday. I described our difficulty and asked his advice. 'You put that bird in charge, and I'll promise you one thing,' Mulligan said. 'He may fail—I don't know anything about that kind of a private outfit—but, by God, it will never be the same school again.' "

I stared at the dean thoughtfully and then said, "His real name is not *Mulligan,* it's *Modjelewski,* and one time he refused —well, it was like that Bible story. He said, 'No, I will not,' but afterward he repented and went."

"I swear," said MacFarland, "have you ever felt a call to the ministry?"

"No," I said, "and I don't expect any. I am going to have my hands full to keep Crampton from going to hell for a while, and after its soul is saved I'll be busy worrying about my own salvation."

There must have been some foreboding and unconscious resentment on my part against the new job, since I found myself meeting the Crampton authorities the next day without any clear plans, even tentative, for solving the school's problems.

I studied the five members of the board and the former headmaster as they told of their difficulties. The chairman, himself a graduate of the institution in the class of 1903, was a lawyer whose social pretensions for a long time had been greater than his income. Two other men, both members of the Crampton family, undoubtedly were in a reverse status; their incomes were adequate, but they were too indolent to have cultivated social or indeed any marked intellectual interests. They, too, were graduates of the school. The other two members were women of the kind then generally known as social leaders; they looked upon board membership as marking their elevated status in the community.

The recently resigned headmaster, Karl Baker Mortensen, was much more interesting to me. He was about forty years old, an obviously sensitive man, whose entire experience had been in private schools. He had come to Crampton in 1915 as a history teacher and had succeeded to the headmastership four years later. He had a baccalaureate and a master's degree from an Eastern university and showed signs of being a scholar. He was almost painfully precise in his description of the faults of his administration. It was a distasteful task for him, but he thought that integrity required his abasement. My first administrative decision, although I did not mention it in the board meeting, was that I would retain Mortensen as a teacher, perhaps making him dean of students.

My second decision followed promptly, and I stated it to the board. I named my salary at a figure considerably above what I had been getting at River Junction. There was a moment of stunned silence, but no objections were raised. Then I said that in the second and third years of my three-year contract I would go on half-time and half-pay; I assumed that after the first year the school would require less administrative attention.

I think the board members were relieved when the meeting ended. They were neither very favorably nor unfavorably impressed by the new administrator, but they were clearly pleased that he seemed to take responsibility readily.

At lunch with the former headmaster, I asked him to stay with the school as a teacher. He floundered a little in response, fearing that his presence on my staff might embarrass me. I laughed carelessly and said, "It takes a lot to embarrass me. I merely ask you always to tell me what is wrong with my administration and then keep quiet about it in public."

He accepted the job, and I wish to state here that he carried it out in a fashion which was brilliant, although only I was in a position fully to recognize that brilliance.

"What is the maximum number of pupils that Crampton can accommodate with its present staff and facilities?" I asked.

"Fifty, or two sections of twenty-five, in each grade," said Mortensen, "—a total enrollment of three hundred."

"And you have about how many in sight for this fall?" I pursued.

"About half that number," he said, "an average of twenty-five per grade, although grade VII will have only fifteen or sixteen."

"And you need at least two hundred enrollments at the present tuition rate to meet the budget?"

Mortensen assented.

"Here is how we'll get two hundred fifty this year and three hundred next year," I said. "First, we'll send an announcement to the newspapers that enrollment at Crampton under the new administration will be strictly limited. Nobody will be admitted who is not entered on our waiting lists."

"We've never needed any waiting lists," said Mortensen mildly. "We've always had plenty of vacancies since I have been at the school."

"All right," I insisted, "but we need waiting lists now. Do you have any relatives, friends, or acquaintances in this city with young children?"

"How young?" he asked.

"Hell, I don't care," I said, but then I added, "The younger the better."

"I've got a sister here who has a four-year-old son," he said, "and I can think of two or three other people I know who have children in the primary grades."

"Good," I said. "Just drop the word that if they might ever want to send those children to Crampton they should call my office and get their names down on the proper list now."

Even after all these years, I am ashamed to recall the success of this tactic. Within thirty days the lists in grades VII for the years 1925 to 1932 were filled. I did not announce this fact publicly, but Mortensen and I dropped discreet hints to our friends that it was going to be more difficult each year to get into the school.

I had a feeling, based on nothing more substantial, probably, than a stereotype of my own, that Crampton was regarded as a sissy school. This seemed to me an almost fatal handicap which I took immediate steps to remove. I began to frequent poolrooms and bowling alleys, asking about the status of boxing, wrestling, and basketball in the city. In a few days a sports reporter called me by telephone, wanting to know some of the details of Crampton's new athletic program, but I was evasive. Finally another reporter showed up who had been in my division in 1917–19. He had exaggerated notions of my own boxing and wrestling achievements. I tried to correct his views, but the mere effort on my part seemed to justify them in his mind. He wrote a piece about the "new Crampton," and I began to get applications for transfers into grades X and XI on behalf of boys who did not seem to be scions of wealth. How could they pay the tuition charges? By doing janitorial and gardening work, I decided. Then some of their feminine friends inquired about the chances of work scholarships for girls, and I manufactured a few for typists and file clerks, of whom teachers never have enough.

We opened the fall term on September 22 with 258 pupils enrolled. The junior high grades ran over the fifty-pupil limit. Grade VII had sixty pupils; grade VIII had fifty-seven; and grade IX, fifty-two. Modifying Crampton policies as casually as I chalked a pool cue, I decided that a maximum of thirty pupils per section was not excessive.

In the senior-high-school grades, most of the new pupils were boys. I looked them over and promptly added football as well as boxing and wrestling to the institution's previous anemic-looking sports program. I coached the three sports myself the first year.

In football I employed a backfield assistant from the Oskaloosa Graduate School. Largely because of his expert knowledge of up-to-date plays, plus a lively morale developed on the squad by two eleventh-graders who had failed to make the local public high-school team the year before, we whipped the team of that rather large school decisively and won a few other games. The wrestling and boxing teams had to go far afield to find high-school opposition, but they too were fairly fortunate in competition.

The only other sport we attempted to engage in on the interscholastic level was track, in which we had a poor record for the spring of 1925. In 1926, with the coaching aid of almost every senior on the university track team we did better, and in 1927 we took highest honors in the state interscholastic meet.

In the academic program, I decided to introduce at least one innovation each year to advance the Crampton record for institutional idiosyncrasy, at least, if not for quality. After studying the faculty's various qualifications, it seemed that foreign language was the place to start. The school had been offering two years of Latin and two years of French. For some reason whose origin was lost in the mist of antiquity no one could study a foreign language until he was at least a ninth-grader. Most pupils took Latin in grades IX and X and French in grades XI and XII. This was so much like the humdrum practice of the public four-year high schools that it seemed as though any change would be an improvement.

Mrs. Aimée Fayard, a native of Besançon, France, was the French teacher. Mrs. Marie Schwartzrauber *née* Hébert, the history and geography teacher in the junior-high-school division, was a graduate of the institution now called the University of Southwestern Louisiana. Her native language was also French. In September, 1924, therefore, we offered French in the seventh grade in addition to the standard four subjects; English, Science, Mathematics, and American History and Geography. Almost half of the entering class elected French—twenty-two pupils. I asked Mrs. Fayard if that size group would be too large for the direct method of teaching, and she responded with a new warmth in her usually reserved Burgundian manner, *"Mais non, mon ami."* One day just before the Christmas holidays, I substituted for her in that seventh-grade French class, and I was astonished by the fluency and verve with which those twelve-and thirteen-year-olds spoke and played and sang in French. They could also read and write the French they spoke.

At the beginning of the second semester, this group had their geography and history in French with Mrs. Schwartzrauber. In the eighth and ninth grades, they took their mathematics with George Landau, a native of Oregon who had minored in French and majored in mathematics at Oskaloosa. In 1927, when they entered the senior division of the school as tenth graders, they had on their records only three years of junior high school French, but they were effectively bi-lingual.

I have often wondered why this relatively simple device for teaching a foreign language thoroughly and economically has not been more often used in secondary schools of the United States. The teachers involved in the program at Crampton liked it. The parents seemed to favor it. The children appeared to be somewhat better informed in the subjects taught in French than were the children who took the same subjects in English, although the difference may well have been caused by the quality of teaching and the *esprit de corps* of the French group. The only adverse criticism of the arrangement, so far as I was aware, came from a few traditionalists who offered such gems as, "How can you expect children to learn proper American history from French books?" and "I should think that learning arithmetic and algebra in French would frustrate those kids thoroughly." To these strictures the teachers replied that the children studied mathematics, history, and geography from the same English-language books that were used in other sections. They also read French books. Then the class discussions, the reports, and the tests were in French. In talking about the American Declaration of Independence, perhaps the French section referred to the *Droits de l'Homme,* but their understanding of the American Revolution seemed thereby to be broadened. To know that, *"La ligne droite est le plus court chemin d'un point à un autre,"* instead of confusing the children, appeared to make, "A straight line is the shortest distance between two points," clear to them.

Thus while the school was acquiring an athletic reputation with the downtown poolroom sports, it was also becoming favorably known to the "French-is-the-language-of-diplomacy" set.

Some of our other attempts to enhance the institution's reputation were not so successful. A biology teacher's Caesarean operation on a cat, as a laboratory demonstration for his tenth-graders, was almost catastrophic, especially in its public-relations aspects for a few days, since the feline mother and all her six progeny failed to survive the ordeal. Although this kind of demonstration was never repeated, the Anti-Vivisection Society kept a grim watch on Crampton for years thereafter.

One of Mortensen's classes in World History had a study project on *Causes of the Great War* (which, in those days, was emphatically a moot subject). The class put on a debate for an assembly program in which the negative team argued that the ambitions of Imperial Germany were not the sole causes of the war. This interested several veterans' groups and other patriotic organizations to the extent that for at least a decade Crampton pupils had a rather undeserved reputation for political liberalism.

In my second and third years at Crampton, the originally planned arrangement for me to be on half-time as the school's administrator did not work very well. As soon as I attempted it in the fall of 1925, I could see that it would not work, and I marveled that I had ever thought it would work. To be involved in an educational institution as a planner, an executive, and an operator of its program demands all the time, attention, and imagination that one can muster.

Since 1925, I have occasionally taken some part-time assignments because I could not avoid them, but the principle thus flouted has always seemed clear. A part-time job, well done, requires full-time effort. A part-time job, given part-time devotion, is necessarily an inferior job.

By working full-time at the university during the summer

quarters of 1926 and 1927, and by cutting my hours for sleep rather sharply in the corresponding winter and spring quarters of those years I was able to complete the necessary course studies and was starting on the dissertation for the doctorate at Oskaloosa.

I had tried in March, 1927, to get Mortensen to take over the Crampton headmastership again for the coming year, but he stoutly refused.

"You can handle this job better than I," I told him. "You are a more polished teacher than I; you know these people; you have all the waiting lists filled."

"No," he said. "I would put some kind of a jinx on the place. I don't feel inferior simply because I am not J. Abner Peddiwell. That doesn't bother me—nobody is Peddiwell."

"Including sometimes Peddiwell himself," I interrupted gloomily.

Mortensen stared at me for a moment and then resumed his argument. "No, what bothers me is that I am Karl Baker Mortensen, and he is not now, never was, and never will be an administrator."

When, a few weeks later, MacFarland and the Crampton board finally agreed to appoint a stranger from another state to the headmastership, Mortensen resigned without comment, taking an instructorship in history at a small college in the upper Mississippi Valley.

By working under forced draft during July and August, 1927, I pushed my doctoral dissertation to the point where I needed only a few weeks in the library of the British Museum. In the summer of 1928 I went to London for that purpose and returned to Oskaloosa in time to take the final oral examination for the doctorate of philosophy. I received the degree on August 29, 1928.

During the academic year 1927–28, however, I had in my first college teaching job certain experiences which modified my behavior somewhat more than graduate study ever did and were therefore more important parts of my education.

SIXTEEN

Dead Coon Lake

ON SEPTEMBER 1, 1927, I was appointed assistant professor of education and psychology at the institution then known as Dead Coon Lake College.

This school had been founded in 1884 in one of the North Central states by certain pioneers who were gathered together in the Lord's name under the title of the Lakeshore Brethren. Dead Coon Lake, a beautiful body of water about ten miles long and two to three miles wide, had several creeks feeding it from little valleys wooded with willow, poplar, and choke-cherry. This was the place where the Brethren had their origin and from which their sect derived its name. A series of summer camp meetings from 1875 until well into the first years of the college's history provided the emotional and intellectual foundations of the denomination. The college, in turn, symbolized and channeled the educational yearnings of the Lakeshore Brethren. It was established on the banks of the lake. Its first classes were held in the campmeeting "hall," a wooden structure which had replaced the original tent in 1882.

The early presidents and many of the faculty members were ministers of the Lakeshore Brethren. The church dreaded the danger of having an illiterate ministry when their current preachers should lie in the dust, as much as did the seventeenth-century residents of the Massachusetts Bay Colony. The Lakeshore Brethren seem never to have pondered the probability that without a nearly illiterate ministry their sect could not have been organized.

When I first saw the Dead Coon Lake College it was nearing the fiftieth year of its history. Its president at that time, John Calvin Johnson, was the first nonclergyman to head the institution. He was a professor of the classics, particularly of Greek, who had been graduated from the college in 1901 and had then gone on, first to Yale for a master's degree, and then to Marburg, that great German fountain of Protestant erudition, where he took his doctorate in 1904. He returned to Dead Coon Lake in the fall of that year as an assistant professor. He had never been a teacher or administrator anywhere except at Dead Coon Lake College.

The college had about forty faculty members in 1927. Only three of them were ministers of the Lakeshore Brethren, but of all the faculty it was one of these clergymen whom I came to know most favorably.

He was James Halvorsen Clark, professor of physics. I think he had no formal preparation for the ministry. In the days of his youth, a member of the Brethren became a clergyman by getting and heading the Call. I do not know anything about Clark's Call or how he served it as a minister. I knew him only as a professor. He had an A.B. degree from Dead Coon Lake (1912) and a master's degree in physics from one of the larger universities of the North Central area.

Every year or two Clark sent a boy to one of the great graduate schools, usually to study chemistry rather than physics. I was later told at Northern State University that any student recommended by Clark was always given one of the top fellowships in the department of chemistry.

"Why?" I asked.

"Because all the people he recommends become distinguished scholars," the chairman of the department explained.

"All?" I repeated. "That's a rather sweeping generalization."

"Yes," agreed the chairman, "it is, but so far there have been no exceptions."

"The Dead Coon Lake boys are smarter than those from other undergraduate colleges?" I hazarded.

"Well, I wouldn't say that," said the professor. "I would say rather that Jim Clark puts a charm on them—or maybe it's a curse. They always seem to work twice as hard and put in twice as many hours as do the other graduate students. If you see a light in the laboratory at 12:30 A.M., it's an easy bet that one of Clark's students is in there working on something. It's usually something the student figured out himself or something suggested to him by Clark."

"But Clark is a physicist," I objected.

"I know," said the chairman, "but he believes that physics and chemistry are indistinguishable in the areas that count most, and all his students act as though he is right. I think, myself, he *is* right."

Clark was one of the most engaging colleagues I ever had. He was full of ideas—whenever you met him—original, hackneyed, imaginative, prejudiced, open-minded, all scattered together in a blooming confusion. Every time I saw him I wanted to stop and get him to tell me anything that was on his mind. Unless I had pressing duties elsewhere, furthermore, I usually yielded to the impulse.

One evening Clark hailed me with a complimentary remark on something I had published. "It's your classical training, Ab," he said. "I tell you that Latin and Greek, or either one of them, are the foundations of English style."

I made the usual modest disclaimer to any style of consequence, but Clark pressed his original point. "Nobody," he continued triumphantly, "ever learns to write English well unless he has studied another language or languages;—particularly ancient languages."

"Does that apply to people whose native language is not English?" I inquired. "French, for example?"

"Sure does," said Clark. "A French writer has simply got to study Latin."

"And a German writer? What foreign language should he study?"

"Latin, too, and Greek. Greek is very good for German writers."

"Has this always been the case?" I persisted.

"Why, certainly," said Clark, "I think so. But you've had more training in history and languages than I, Ab. Isn't my idea correct?"

"Well," I said, "it certainly applied to the great Latin writers. Practically all of them had studied Greek."

"That's right," agreed the professor enthusiastically.

"And what foreign language did the Greek writers of classical antiquity study?" I inquired.

"I don't know," replied Clark, a shade of hesitation entering his tone. "Persian, I guess, or maybe Egyptian. Xenophon must have known some Persian."

"Yes," I assented. "Doughboy Persian perhaps. But unfortunately the great Athenian writers and orators knew no language whatever except Greek. Sophocles, Euripides, Pericles, Plato, Polybius, Sappho—none of them ever studied a foreign language. Interpreters and translators were all slaves. It was a menial task to figure out barbarian speech or writing."

Clark looked stricken. "Are you sure of that, Ab?" he asked.

"Well, fairly sure," I said, "but you're probably right in your general theory. Those ancient Greeks were undoubtedly exceptional people in that as in other ways."

"I'm *not* right," declared Clark decisively. "It's just another one of my theories that hasn't got a fact to stand on."

"But consider"—I began to seek arguments for Clark's original view—"consider the case of old Ben Franklin, the finest all-around American writer of his era. He taught himself and learned to write French very well."

"Uh-huh," said Clark gloomily, "but consider also the author of the Gettysburg Address. How much French or any other foreign language did *he* know?"

Thus we ended with our initial positions reversed. This happened oftener with Clark than with any other professor I have ever known. It is easy for me to see why the students he sent to graduate school were conspicuously successful. They carried a potent *wakan*. I do not know what it was, but I know it came from James Halvorsen Clark.

He put some of that *wakan* on me. If I were today an eighteen-year-old boy wanting to study physical science and if Clark were teaching at Dead Coon Lake I would seek entrance to that institution even though it had twenty former Rhodes scholars on its staff cooking up a new system of tutorials; forty professors in the humanities, the arts, and the social sciences concocting new courses in general studies; sixty personnel and guidance experts with new testing and counseling programs; eighty—but wait a moment! Clark is dead, the Dead Coon Lake school has become Lake College-by-the-Woods, and it does not have eighty people on its whole faculty.

We had at Dead Coon Lake in those days about three hundred students. The college conferred approximately fifty A.B. degrees each year, and more than half of these graduates completed the requirements for secondary-school teachers' certificates. Because I had the responsibility of seeing these students through educational psychology, secondary-school methods, and student teaching, I felt that the college was a teacher-training institution at least as much as it was anything else.

This was a basic heresy of which I was at first unaware. President Johnson was convinced that the college was primarily a place for the general education of leaders. By *leaders* he meant lawyers, bankers, physicians, merchants, and clergymen, in that order. Dean Torgersholm thought it was an institution for passing on a mystical torch of higher learning from cultivated to cultivable hands. The various branches of learning, headed by philosophy, were strictly ranked in his mind. Education was not at the bottom, but it was near it. The absolute nadir to him was occupied by home economics and physical education. His favorite references concerning these two bottom subjects were to doctoral dissertations somewhere on dishwashing and weight lifting.

I took the position that I would have to read those dissertations in order to see whether they appeared to be as valuable in their contribution to knowledge as others, for example, in the dating of key plays in the Restoration drama or the use of the ablative absolute in Petronius' *Satyricon.* I mentioned further the observation that I should know at least as much about home economics and physical education as I knew about the English and Latin literatures before hazarding even a tentative judgment on the relative quality of the research reports involved.

My colleague, Flint, himself a saturnine native of New England, with graduate degrees from Harvard and Columbia Universities, came warmly to my support. "Style is what determines quality in research of any kind," he said. "I don't mean just style of exposition, although that does enter the picture. I mean also, and more importantly, the style of study, of designing the research, of delimiting a problem, of getting data, and of drawing conclusions. If weight lifting and dishwashing are topics about which people in physical education and home economics want and need to learn more, why shouldn't they study those topics scientifically?"

I realize now that, by the time this discussion was occurring, the beginning of my third year and Flint's fourth year in the college, both of us had effectively solidified our status. We could never be promoted to higher academic grades under that administration. We would not be discharged or even reprimanded. We were doing too important a part of the college's work, but we had to be kept at our current grades because the part we did was not sufficiently honorific.

At the time, Flint and I did not understand this fact, and so were reasonably happy. I have long since come to see that our cases were amply covered by the classic administrative principle, *De decanibus nihil nisi reverentiam,* which any competent Latinist will tell you means, "Don't get gay with the deans unless you want to be an assistant professor forever."

I must take the chief blame for finally putting both Flint and myself in the permanent academic doghouse. I proposed establishing what I called a *Public School Reference Bureau* as a service agency for school districts. It was not a very original notion in 1930. Various teacher-education institutions already had agencies of this kind. The idea at Dead Coon Lake was that Flint and I would help reorganize schools, construct new curricula, even survey school systems, getting special assistance from people in neighboring colleges and universities, the state department of education, and larger city administrative and supervisory staffs. I was enthusiastic about the possibilities of the enterprise. I wrote an elaborate description of the planned bureau and sent copies to President Johnson, Dean Torgersholm, the state commissioner of education, and Dean MacFarland at Oskaloosa. I feel certain that President Johnson never read my prospectus. Dean Torgersholm read it hurriedly after the state commissioner and MacFarland had called it to his attention by sending him enthusiastic comments on it.

I suppose Torgersholm must have discussed the matter, however briefly, with the the president of the college. At least, I got that impression from the official conversation in which I was told by the dean that the college was not interested in this kind of "extension" activity. I thought that loyalty to my college and my department required me to argue warmly for my proposal, but my warmth did not melt any ice from the dean's disapproval. Flint was somewhat more heated than I in his comments. I was beginning to feel that as his department chairman I was leading him into an academic wilderness.

Both of us were personally fortunate in this situation. We were young enough to move, and we were in that part of the United States, the North Central area, where at that time higher education was undoubtedly the most advanced. Flint went in September, 1930, to one of the great universities of the area as an associate professor of psychology. At the same time, I went to the

Northern State University as associate professor of education. President Johnson had to resign from Dead Coon Lake College in 1932. The economic depression had hit the institution, and the president's liberalism and Yale-Marburg reminiscences were at last deemed inadequate by the Dead Coon Board of Trustees.

The board promptly elected as Johnson's successor a Rhodes scholar who persuaded it without much difficulty to adopt a system of tutorial instruction and to drop *Dead Coon* from the institution's official name. Neither of these measures was powerful enough to offset the continuing impact of the depression, but the various Federal aids then available to colleges were eagerly proffered by representatives of alphabetical agencies and as eagerly grasped by the president.

After World War II, the Rhodes scholar was replaced in the president's office by an earnest young man with a Ph. D. degree in the humanities, a rather broad area being developed in only two graduate schools at that time. He promptly instituted a program of general studies in the four great fields of physical sciences, biological sciences, social sciences, and the humanities. He also got the board to add *by-the-Woods* to the official name of the college. The legislature gave state sanction to the new title by amending the articles of incorporation to that effect in its 1947 session. By 1947, furthermore, the pioneer willow, poplar, and choke-cherry growths were being over-shadowed by imported oak, sour gum, maple, and other more academically respectable trees. At that time, no higher educational institution with a program of general studies could possibly be considered dead. In 1947 it was actually in the forefront of educational thought. The new name was consequently appropriate.

I must admit, however, that even today whenever I hear or see, *Lake College-by-the-Woods,* I perversely think, *Dead Coon.*

I do not know what, if anything, has happened to the Lakeshore Brethren. I have not seen one for years. They may have succumbed to the effects of over-schooling. The catalog of *Lake College-by-the-Woods,* in the section called *History,* no longer specifically mentions the *Brethren* as the founding fathers. In fact, the more the college has emphasized its general studies, the vaguer its references to its origins have become. Whether I have here the nucleus of an important principle in general education or merely a minor item in history of higher learning on the shores of Dead Coon Lake is a problem which I leave to the reader.

Perhaps I would do better at this point to remember what might well be an ancient French proverb, *Laissez coucher les raccoons morts.*

SEVENTEEN

Northern State University

WHEN I WENT to Northern State University in September, 1930, Poplar Branch Handelman had been president of the institution for two years. In my nine years at Northern I taught various courses, developed my specialty of comparative education, served as assistant and acting dean of the College of Education, and worked at several administrative tasks in connection with the state and Federal governments' efforts to deal educationally with the so-called Great Depression. My chief activity in that nine-year period, however, it is now clear to me, was the critical study under Handelman's guidance of a university's purposes, functions, and practices.

My introduction to the president was in itself a marked educational experience. As soon as I arrived on the campus, about a week before the beginning of the fall quarter, I reported to the office of Dean Henry H. Butler of the College of Education. His secretary said, "The dean is in Europe." Before I could ask the obvious question concerning the date of his return, the girl added hastily, "The president wants to see you as soon as possible."

I was not personally acquainted with Handelman. I had seen him and heard him speak at national and state meetings of teachers and school administrators. He had been professor of educational administration at Oskaloosa and dean of the College of Education at Northern State before becoming president. I did not suppose, however, that he had ever seen me or heard of me.

In the early spring of 1930, I had been interviewed by Dean Butler and had met several members of the education faculty. When the dean offered me an associate professorship, I accepted it swiftly and gratefully. Nobody mentioned President Handelman to me until I was back at Dead Coon Lake retailing the news to my friend, Jim Clark.

"Northern State," commented Clark. "Isn't that where Poplar Branch Handelman is president?"

I said it was.

"You are lucky," continued Clark. "That man is a great administrator."

"I don't suppose I'll see much of him," I remarked.

"Why not?" asked Clark.

"Well, I'll be only an associate professor on a campus with more than twelve thousand students," I explained. "Here, as an assistant professor in a college with fewer than five hundred students, I didn't see the president very often."

"No?" said Clark. "And you were a department chairman here too."

"I dealt with Dean Torgersholm in connection with departmental business," I insisted. "At Northern State I'll have no administrative duties."

Clark looked skeptical. "That is what you think," he remarked and let the matter drop.

Now as I walked over to Handelman's office, I wondered uneasily what he wanted to see me about. I do not think I remembered Jim Clark's earlier comment at that time. I was a trifle astonished that the president of a university as large as Northern State had a personal conference with each newly appointed faculty member.

At the president's office I was further startled by the warmth of the reception tendered me. As soon as I mentioned my name to the president's personal secretary, a statuesque blonde whose deskplate proclaimed her to be *Miss Marie Desjardins,* she came to a ladylike attention with every indication that I was an important caller, shook hands politely, and said, "The president will be delighted to know that you are here."

I did not see Miss Desjardins touch a signal button. Perhaps Handelman had especially acute hearing or unusual psychic powers. Whatever the cue, the door to his inner office opened at once and he emerged with outstretched hand. "Come in, come in," he said. "I'm sure glad you're here early." He spoke with the slow but incisive drawl of a Westerner.

The president came by his Western accent naturally. His father had been a roving cattlebuyer in Idaho, Montana, and the Dakotas who packed his family around with him and named his children after their birthplaces. Thus the two older sons were *Boise North* and *Butte West* respectively. The daughter was *Laramie East*. When the youngest boy was born he missed being called *Bad Lands South* by a narrow margin. He appeared unexpectedly at a camp on an unnamed branch of Poplar Creek in northeastern Montana. His mother stoutly resisted the addition of *Southwest* to his names to indicate the general direction in which the original Poplar branch ran. "This is my last baby," she said firmly, "and I don't aim to have him stuck in one corner of the map the rest of his days!"

Handelman was as unusual in many ways, important and unimportant, as were his first and middle names. In 1930 he was fifty-five years old, and he stepped around as lightly as a middleweight boxer. His shoulders seemed to strain his coat whenever he moved his arms. In his youth he had been a professional ballplayer, a catcher. I think he was a good one, although he never made the majors.

On this, my first appearance in the president's office, as well as in all later interviews with him, he came directly to the point with a minimum of preliminaries. I never knew another man who could appear and be so expansive and easygoing yet get important business done so fast.

"Dean Butler is in Europe," he began.

"Yes, sir," I said. "His secretary told me. When will he be back?"

"Next June," said Handelman. "He is studying British universities. I am therefore appointing you acting dean of the College of Education for the academic year, 1930–31."

I was so astonished that I had no room for modesty or timidity, and the president gave me no time to develop either one. I said something to the effect that the College of Education had a number of well-known professors with backgrounds of excellent administrative experience who could handle such an assignment better than I.

The president listened politely and in relaxed manner, but as soon as I paused he moved swiftly to his point. "They are all members of special political groupings, academic combinations, and plain cliques," he said suavely. (He pronounced the final word, *clicks*.) "You are not. I know about your work at River Junction and at Crampton. I know what you did for the student teachers at Dead Coon Lake and tried to do for the cooperating school districts in that area." Here he added a few details in a manner that was factually forthright and subtly complimentary. I did not realize it at the time, but I was being introduced to a new job by a great administrator, the most skillful of his era. Within fifteen minutes I was back in the office of the dean of the College of Education, studying the budget and just beginning to be frightened.

In retrospect I cannot speak too warmly of the professors in the College of Education. Undoubtedly they had their *clicks*, as Handelman called them, but they treated me with the utmost consideration. Any two or three of them could have made my job impossible. Instead, they all worked together to make it fairly simple. All the full professors and most of the associate professors were my seniors in experience and professional achievements, yet none showed a sign of dragging his feet or being in any way a prima donna. Inexperienced though I was, I knew enough about universities to be aware of the polish of these feuding professors' manners. It seemed as though their code imposed an ethic which stated in effect, *All quarrels stop at the acting dean's door.*

One morning, after the fall quarter had been under way for

six weeks, the dean's secretary informed me as I came into the office from teaching an early class that the president would like to have me attend the meeting of the Board of Regents.

"When does the board meet?" I inquired anxiously.

"It's meeting now," she said, "in that big room next to the president's office. He wants you to go right in."

I picked up a copy of the college budget and hurried toward the Administration Building. I could think only of financial questions requiring my attendance at a meeting of the regents.

The board had fifteen members, including the president, and only one was absent that day. Handelman, as ex-officio chairman of the board, was presiding. He introduced me and then seated me at the end of the table opposite him, with seven board members lined in easy chairs along one side and six along the other. Over against the wall, to my left, seated in hard chairs, as a small but select audience, were two elderly deans, Bowman of Agriculture and Hansen of Arts and Sciences. They looked at me with what seemed like sly grins.

Probably because I was frightened, I sat stiffly at unconscious military attention, an ironic posture to assume in view of the later discussion.

As usual, the president wasted no words in preliminaries. "This is a land-grant university," he said, "and as such it requires male undergraduate students to take military drill."

"Excuse me, Mr. President," interposed one of the regents, a mousy-looking man who, I learned later, was the chief founder of the state's Farmer-Labor Party. "This is a land-grant university and as such it is required to *offer* instruction in military drill."

"All right, all right," said the president brusquely. "Anyway, we all agree that it *is* a land-grant university and it *does* require male undergraduates who are physically fit to receive two years of training in military science and tactics." He glared at me. "You know the system, Dean?" he demanded.

"Not very well," I said uneasily.

"You're a graduate of a land-grant university," he commented accusingly. "Didn't you take the drill yourself?"

"No, sir," I said.

"You were physically fit?" he persisted. I could feel my face warming a little at this relentless inquisition.

"Well, er, I was excused because of previous military service," I explained stiffly.

"Ah, all the better," said the president. "You know more about it than most of us."

"I don't know much about it," I said hesitantly. "I believe that all land-grant institutions have compulsory military training."

"All except one," said Handelman, and he named the school. "The board of that university," he continued, "has just got a court decision that a land-grant institution is required to offer instruction in military science and tactics but is not required to make it compulsory for any student. We now have a motion before this board to adopt the same policy at Northern State. We have called in several witnesses." He glanced hostilely at Deans Bowman and Hansen. "It occurred to me that you are the only dean in this university who has had recent active military experience and that you are the only member of the faculty outside the department of military science and tactics, so far as I know, who has been a Regular Army officer. I thought we ought to get your views."

I was chilled by a swift foreknowledge of what was likely to happen, and in cowardly fashion, I tried to avoid it.

"I was only a lieutenant," I said. "I was an enlisted man much longer than I was an officer."

"A *first* lieutenant," emphasized the president, "promoted to that rank on the field of battle and decorated ..."

I could feel the blood boiling into my forehead and ears as I interrupted. "I paid little attention to military instruction at the university where I was an undergraduate," I said hastily. "I have never been a faculty member in a land-grant college or university except just here this fall."

"You must have some ideas about military training," said Handelman with what I interpreted as sarcasm. I promptly felt my modesty and the excess blood in my face ebbing away simultaneously.

"Yes, I have," I said.

"Have you seen any of our military instruction here?" he asked.

"From my office window," I replied, "I have observed the students learning close-order drill and the manual-of-arms. I saw them passing in review last Friday, doing eyes right, with sergeants counting cadence and cadet officers flourishing sabers in what they thought were salutes."

"What do you think of it?" demanded my inquisitor.

"I think it is a kind of exercise for them," I said. "Some of them probably enjoy it."

"But don't you think it is good training for national defense, good character formation, good education in patriotism?"

"No," I said coldly. I thought I would tell the truth and take my chances of getting another associate professorship in June. I started to elaborate my position, but Handelman again interposed a question.

"How can you say that?" he snorted. "You haven't made any real study of our military department!"

"Mr. President," began the mousy-looking man, but he was not speaking in mousy fashion. "You qualified the dean as an expert witness and yet you presume to interrupt him when his testimony does not agree with your own inexpert views. Suppose we let him finish what he started to say."

"Right! Right!" growled Handelman. "Excuse me, Dean. Go ahead."

"I am just commenting on close-order drill and the manual-of-arms," I said with my embarrassment starting to return. "Most of their supposed values are based on a belief in a thoroughly outmoded faculty psychology. They were demonstrated useless in battle long ago."

"Long ago?" repeated the irrepressible president.

"As long ago as that day on the Monongahela when Major-General Sir Edward Braddock gave his exhausted men a stiff dose of manual-of-arms as they staggered out of the woods and then tried to keep them in close order while an inferior force of French and Indian skirmishers cut them to pieces." By this time my embarrassment had been completely engulfed by a rising tide of irritation at this whole stupid civilian inquiry.

"The question here, as I understand it," I went on, "is whether to make your military instruction, which I am sure includes much more valuable activity than squads-right-and-left, compulsory or voluntary. I recommend strongly that you make it voluntary. You'll get better reserve officers that way. You spoke of my not having made any study of your military department. I'll be glad to make such a study and show your officers and the administration of the university how to set up a real college of military science. With such a college you would have young men clamoring for admission to the program instead of organizing peace strikes against it."

The president stared bleakly around the table. "Are there any further questions the board members wish to ask the dean?" he inquired. About ten of the members smiled at me and shook their heads. The other three members looked sadly at the president. Hanson and Bowman beamed impartially around the room. I found out later that both of them had recommended making the drill optional. I also learned later that the final vote was eleven to two in favor of abolishing the compulsory requirement on a trial basis for four years. The president himself had suggested the compromise and had asked for its unanimous approval. The two regents who stuck to their *no* votes did so on purely patriotic grounds into which no logical argument was allowed to intrude.

At the time, however, Handelman merely stood up and said, "Thank you, Mr. Dean."

"It was my pleasure, Mr. President," I said woodenly and left the room.

I started down the hallway, haunted by a feeling of frustrated anger. I hated the president for putting me in such a situation without warning; I hated the board for failing to make up its collective mind by its own efforts; and above all I hated myself for an inadequate statement and especially for its boastful ending. I had said either too much or too little, probably both simultaneously.

I heard a door, further down the hall, open behind me. Quick steps appeared to be overtaking me. In my current state of mind I paid them little heed. Then the president spoke at my elbow, his hand outstretched.

"I sure appreciated what you did under pressure," he said, with every appearance of sincerity, "and just because I was on the other side of the argument I hope you don't hold it against *me*."

I was so astonished that I forgot my anger and embarrassment. "Why, hell," I said, "I hope you won't hold it against *me*."

The clearly expressed wonder in the man's eyes showed me in a flash that his apparent sincerity was very real. "Hah! No," he said. "I wanted an expert's views and, by God, I got 'em."

Then he laughed, the same kind of booming, roughneck laugh he used in baseball, shook hands once more, and was gone back to the board meeting.

I do not pretend to understand how the president's artistry operated. I merely know that thereafter to the end of his life I never had any doubt about Poplar Branch Handelman's motives. They were always as clear as glass and as straight as a plumbline. I gave him my views whenever he asked for them and sometimes when he did not want them but I thought he could use them and should have them, and I never again had a moment's concern that he would count them against me. Poplar Branch Handelman was not that kind of administrator.

Like every good administrator, however, the president was a fighter who valued victory and consequently was not above seeking and using the optimum tactic for a particular situation and mission.

As an example, he did not forget my offer to make a study of the military department at Northern. He never asked for such a study, but toward the end of my first year at Northern he did have me investigate the instructional methods employed in the department of civil engineering in the university's Institute of Technology.

"I think you're probably more expert in the field of instructional methods than you are in military training," he said bluntly. "Anyway, I'd like to have you observe everybody of professorial rank in civil engineering and report their methods to me in such detail as you think proper."

"You don't want me to rate them?" I suggested.

"No," he said, *"I'll* rate them on the basis of the facts in your report."

Already I knew Handelman well enough not to ask any further questions. If I had inquired, for example, "How am I going to get all those professors to cooperate with me in this study?" he would undoubtedly have said something like, "Hah! That's *your* problem."

In reality I found that the professors of civil engineering were very cooperative. They treated me with utmost courtesy. Two years later, after I had become personally acquainted with some of them I found that before I was assigned to the task the president had talked to all of the civil-engineering faculty members, singly or in small groups, carefully preparing them in extended discussions for the kind of study I was asked to make. The need for the study had arisen from the formation of three main *clicks* in that department with charges and countercharges of poor teaching being tossed back and forth among them. It was characteristic of Handelman to move directly to the heart of these charges. The ordinary university administrator in such a situation practically always pulls, hauls, and hesitates. He lacks the two chief administrative resources which Handelman always seemed to have in full measure: (1) precise knowledge of the problem and (2) the will to solve it.

When Dean Butler returned from Europe in the summer of 1931, he was kind in his comments on my service as acting dean and informed me that he was recommending me for promotion to a professorship. I thanked him, somewhat astonished to have served as associate professor only a year, and said something to the effect that I would try to get a book finished soon in order to deserve the promotion. He laughed easily.

"We don't recommend so much on the basis of books here as we do on action," he remarked.

"Action?" I repeated, mystified.

"Yes," he said, "the president, as you have probably noted, is rather active himself, and he prizes any tendency of a professor to get things done, even though the professor may try to do some things the president doesn't want done."

"Well, I tried to carry out the university's—er—" I began, and the dean laughed again.

"Yes?" he said. "The president went so far as to recommend to me that I recommend to him your promotion. Of course, he didn't phrase it exactly that way. What he actually said was, 'I had to step lively to keep the Board of Regents from passing a resolution to have me instruct that boy to study the military department and tell us how to make a great College of Military Science out of it. We have to give him enough rank so he'll be a little easier to keep track of.'"

Perhaps the closest view I ever had of Handelman's tactics was one I experienced during my third year of service at Northern State. For some special reason which I have now forgotten, I was acting as the president's administrative aid. In that capacity I went with him to the legislature to appear before a joint meeting of the senate and house committees on education.

The chairman of the senate committee, Per Bloomquist of Talking Lake County, was presiding. He was a Republican. His party had a majority in the Senate; the Farmer-Labor Party held the majority in the House. The presiding officer opened the meeting with a statement of cold precision. Even his pronounced Swedish intonation could not disguise his meaning.

"Ve got hare before us, yentlemen," he said, "de proposed budget of de Nordern State Juniwersity. If anybody has forgot his copy de clerk got some extra vuns. Ay'll yust say before ve call any vitnesses dot dis budget is too large. Nordern State is not Harward, and it is not de Juniwersity of California. It is a juniwersity in a state dot has a lot of hungry people. Ve small business men and especially ve poor farmers in dis state are already taxed more dan ve can bear. Dis budget *got* to be reduced. Ve have hare dis morning de president of Nordern State, vid vun of his young men, and ve ask him now, *how is he going to cut dis budget?*"

The senator's icy gaze flickered over me as he made his contemptuous reference to the president's young assistant and then returned to Handelman and remained there unblinkingly as he waited for an answer. Four or five newsmen in the back of the room scribbled busily on their writing pads. As soon as Handelman started to reply, they stopped writing and joined the rest of the occupants of the room in giving him undivided attention.

"You tell me how much to cut the budget and I will report your wishes to the board of regents and show them how the cut can best be made," the president said smoothly.

"Dis is no answer, Dr. Handelman," said Bloomquist. "Ve are not authorities on de juniwersity budget. Ve don't know how much it can be cut. You are de expert. *You* tell us."

"Hah!" snorted the president roughly. "I will be glad to tell you. There are two ways to cut a university budget. The first way is to reduce funds for all the departments, all the colleges and services, by a required percentage, say ten per cent. This is a stupid method. It reduces the quality of the total university effort by ten per cent. You now have a whole institution that is inferior to the one you had last year. The second way to cut the budget by a required amount, again, let us say ten per cent, is to eliminate a whole department, an entire service, until the cut of ten per cent is reached. This is an intelligent way to reduce the budget because the departments and services you have left after the cut are just as good as they were last year. You may indeed be able to improve them, and as a matter of good policy they should be improved or they will deteriorate. Any higher educational institution that starts resting on its oars is liable to go to hell downstream. You tell me what departments, colleges, and services you are willing to have removed from the university program and what per cent reduction you want reached, and I will go to the Regents with the necessary technical details for obeying the legislature's orders."

"But dis is ridiculous," stormed Bloomquist. "Hare Ay am, a poor farmer who only had four yares of schooling in de old country, and Ay have trouble talking English; and hare you are a high educated man dot ve hire at good vages to be our big expert on de juniwersity, and you try to make *me* say vot to cut out of de juniwersity program."

"Exactly," said Handelman. "You have been a member of this legislature for over twenty years, and you have studied the university budgets item by item every biennium. You represent our employers, the people of this state. You are elected by that group of our people who live in Talking Lake County. If you don't know the university's program, you should know it. Now I am asking you to tell me what part of that program your people want eliminated."

Again the newsmen were writing rapidly. The senator seemed visibly shaken by Handelman's insistence. "Vell, you put it dot vay, and Ay am villing to say, 'Vy don't you cut out some of dese useless, high-toned subjects dot nobody ever needs for any practical purpose?' "

"Like what, for instance?" demanded the president.

"Vell, like dis hare Greek you have at the juniwersity," replied the senator. "De students don't even learn to talk Greek so dot dey can order ham and eggs in a Greek eating place."

"All right," said Handelman, "We can eliminate Greek, but we certainly won't save much money by that kind of cut. Greek is one of the cheapest subjects to teach in the university. You can hire an instructor in elementary Greek for a very small salary. Any room with a blackboard will do for a Greek class. The students buy their own texts and grammars. You can look on page 112 of the budget and see how little we would save by eliminating Greek from the Department of Ancient Languages and Literature. But I'll recommend it to the regents if you so instruct me. And when the professors in the Lutheran Seminary on the other side of the city complain that the pre-theological undergraduate program at Northern State no longer includes Greek, and they ask me how a Lutheran minister who lacks the ability to read the Greek New Testament in the original tongue can hope to expound the Gospel properly, I will refer them to Senator Bloomquist. I will say, 'The people of this state don't care anything about clergymen or whether they can read a Greek Testament.' "

"Vait a minute, vait yoost vun little minute," said the senator. "You know Ay never t'ought dot. Now you are yoking me, and Ay don't t'ink dot yoke is very funny! Ve have yoked long enough. You've had your yoke, and now Ay vant to know how you recommend to cut dis budget."

I was astonished by Handelman's swift response and totally unprepared for it, as everyone else seemed to be. "All right, I'll tell you," he said with an almost savage emphasis, raising his voice and leaning forward across the table. "You want to cut the budget significantly? Cut out the Department of Animal Husbandry in the College of Agriculture. Talk about saving money! That's the way to do it. You can't hire a good Ph. D. in animal husbandry for less than $6,500 a year, and you can't teach that stuff in an ordinary classroom with a piece of chalk and a textbook either. You have to buy bulls, so help me! Last year we paid eighteen thousand bucks for one mangy bull! Hah!'"

"Vait vun more minute," cried Bloomquist in a voice of real anguish. "Dot vas not a mangy bull. Dot bull is a national champion. He means a lot more to us poor farmers and stockmen dan any few t'ousand dollars he cost. Vid dis new artificial-insemination program, dot bull is going to mean at de least vun hundred t'ousand dollars per yare in de vestern part of dis state alone. No! You are yoost yoking again!'"

I remember that, even in my concern for what I thought was a profound quarrel developing between these two powerful figures, I had a momentary sense of wonder that the senator who had so much apparent difficulty with relatively simple English words should reel off expressions like *artificial-insemination program* with hardly a trace of accent.

Handelman listened impassively and then answered with cold emphasis, "I am *not* joking, and I was not joking when we were talking about Greek and pre-theological instruction and reading the New Testament in the original. You want to cut the budget, and I am telling you how to do it."

The final vote of the combined committee was to recommend passage of the university budget as submitted by the regents.

As the president and I were riding back to the campus, he said mildly, "Bloomquist is a good man, don't you think?"

"I was startled by the vehemence with which he opened the discussion," I said. "I thought he was going to be very difficult."

Handelman was genuinely surprised. "Oh," he commented, "Bloomquist is a good politician. He always has to get into the record a clear statement that he is for the poor farmer and the suffering taxpayer. He and I usually put on some kind of an act each session. We have dinner together and block it out a week or two before the legislature opens. We try to teach the members of those committees, and (through the newspapers) the public, at least one new principle of university organization and support each biennium. You saw what we attempted this year. Two years from now I think we'll hit university extension and adult education. I'll appreciate any suggestions on it. I think next time *I* should be more conservative and have the senator bring *me* to reason."

I am afraid that I may be picturing Poplar Branch Handelman as an ever cool and calculating character, when, on a matter of real import, he was more often a sentimental dreamer. To illustrate, I'll give you my memory of a seemingly minor incident which must have assumed great meaning to me or I would not be remembering it so clearly after more than thirty years.

One of the university faculty dinner clubs at Northern State was innocuously named *The Wine and Dine Society*. It was composed entirely of professors or former professors. It had a maximum of forty members, with no more than two from each department. Thus there were two professors of medicine, two of law, two of history, two of engineering, and so on, with some smaller departments having only one member. The Society had ten monthly meetings annually. The program was always of the same pattern—a dinner in a private club downtown with table wine the only drink permitted, followed by a paper read by one of the members. This paper was either from the professor's field of academic specialization or from another field which he regarded as his main hobby. No outside speaker was ever invited although outside guests were occasionally permitted.

Handelman, as a member, invited me to a Wine-and-Dine meeting in the fall of 1931 after I had become a full professor. I enjoyed the dinner and looked forward to hearing the paper after we had gathered around the fireplace in the library of the club.

The chairman for the evening was a professor of plant pathology, but he introduced the speaker with learned references to eighteenth- and early nineteenth-century philosophers in Germany and a few other countries and to various contributions the speaker had made to a better understanding of those philosophers. "We are deeply privileged," he continued, "to have this great scholar as a member of our society and as professor of philosophy and chairman of the department of philosophy in this university. He has prepared a paper entitled *Certain Reflections on Julius Langbehn's 'Rembrandt als Erzieher.'* It is an honor, for which I am deeply grateful, to present Dr. Nels Holgersen to the Society, or rather to present the Society to Dr. Holgersen."

The tall, gaunt Holgersen stood up and all the members arose and applauded warmly. Holgersen said calmly and politely, as though it were a common experience for him to have his audience rise to greet him, "Please be seated, gentlemen." I remember those four words quite clearly because they were about the last four words which I comprehended that evening. Without any ordinary-language preliminary, he launched into what was perhaps a vigorous and critical discussion of the topic. He spoke English, with many long German quotations from *"Rembrandt als Erzieher,"* but I could understand the German as well as the English, which was to say practically not at all. I thought I knew, for example, the exact meaning of *"Rembrandt als Erzieher,"* and I fancied that this work would be of special interest to a professor of education, but Holgersen's first sentence disabused me of that naïve notion. That sentence ran over one full typewritten page. I was sitting only ten feet from the professor and verified this fact by direct observation. The sentence went ten lines on the second page before it reached a period. Most of his sentences were shorter. I judged them to average about seventy-five words. I cannot blame my lack of comprehension on the length of sentences, however. I could not have understood the professor if his sentences had averaged only six or seven words, I made those estimates of length not in any spirit of criticism but merely to interest myself in something until the paper ended.

It took just fifty minutes for the professor to read his paper. He sat down to a second round of thunderous applause from the standing members. "Thank you, gentlemen," he murmured politely, and I noted that here was a block of three words which I understood clearly.

The presiding member then made a special speech of thanks. "Professor Holgersen," he said, "treated a very important topic in his usual brilliant and scholarly manner, and we are deeply grateful to him. He has very kindly offered to answer any questions we may have on his contribution."

Holgersen, in his flat, rather monotonous voice, murmured something modestly that had the word *try* in it, and all the members of the society laughed appreciatively at his wit. Then I noticed he was rigging up a black box on the table, with earphones for himself, and I realized that he was deaf. Even thirty years ago that box arrangement was a long way behind the hearing-aid times, but a professor of engineering and a professor of medicine hovered at the speaker's side to be of assistance in this important project. Finally, after testing the apparatus, Holgersen gave the go-ahead signal and the chairman again called for questions. A young professor of comparative literature thereupon got to his feet. First, he paid a glowing tribute to the lecturer. Then he asked for one minor clarification. It took a little over ten minutes to phrase the question, and so far as I could see it was just as clear as Holgersen's paper—no more and no less. I understood none of it.

I gathered that Holgersen said the question was profoundly significant. It took him about fifteen minutes to answer it. Then the second questioner arose, a professor of Central European History. Like his predecessor he first spoke of his indebtedness and that of all instructed people to Professor Holgersen for this paper. Also like his predecessor he had a minor matter on which he desired the master's comment. This too was a very important point, said Holgersen, and he would do his best to answer it. The question and the answer were again totally incomprehensible to me.

By this time we had given about two hours to the miserable Julius Langbehn and his work on *"Rembrandt als Erzieher."* The chairman asked if there were any more questions. There appeared to be none, so he thanked Dr. Holgersen once more, and everybody stood up once more and applauded loudly. Then the meeting was adjourned, whereupon all the members formed a queue to shake hands with the lecturer and shout (because the black box did not work very well), "Thank you for a wonderful paper, Dr. Holgersen. Your contribution was tremendous."

I stood aside and pondered such obvious facts as (1) the faculty members at Northern State University or at least those in this Wine-and-Dine organization were much more formally polite than professors in other universities; (2) they had much better education on Langbehn than I; (3) I must have lost a great deal of my hearing skill not only in German but also in English; and (4) it would be hypocritical of me to compliment Holgersen on something I did not understand. At the last, however, I could see I was going to be too conspicuous if I stayed out of the congratulatory queue, so I fell into line. "Thank you, Professor Holgersen," I shouted. "I am Peddiwell, a new man here in education."

"Thank you, Professor Peddiwell, for listening to a paper that was really not very important," he said, and suddenly I could feel myself warming to him. *Why, hell,* I thought, *this man is not fooled by all that praise.*

As President Handelman was preparing to drive me home, he slid behind the wheel of his car and said, "You liked Holgersen, I could see."

"Yes, sir," I said, "but my background is not very good on such matters, and I did not understand that paper. I had never heard of Langbehn before, either."

Handelman laughed in his rough manner. "Hell's Bells," he guffawed. "Nobody knew what Holgersen was talking about."

"The chairman of the meeting and those two professors who asked questions at the end—they seemed well informed," I said.

"Ho, ho!" chuckled the president, "they've been studying that damn' *'Rembrandt als Erzieher'* and a biography of that bird, Langbehn, for three or four weeks. They were picked for their jobs last month."

"But everybody was thanking Holgersen so sincerely," I began, "that I thought—"

"Sure," said the president. "I thanked him, and I was sincere. We were all sincere. We were just thanking him again for being Nels Holgersen, a big man, and I am not referring to his height." Then he told me Holgersen's story.

In 1917 an ultra-patriotic board of regents at Northern State had dismissed a professor of German for pro-German sentiments and utterances, all of which had been expressed prior to April 6, 1917, and the U.S. declaration of war against Germany. After that date the professor said he would support his adopted country loyally. Up to that date, however, he had consistently argued, not in his classes but in various public discussions, for support of Germany and against alignment with Britain and France.

"So the regents fired him," said Handelman. "I wasn't the president then or even on the faculty at Northern, but if I had been I probably would have been scared of the regents just as the president and the faculty were in 1917. Everybody was scared—everybody except Nels Holgersen. He had been down in Washington on a Sabbatical, working in the Library of Congress, maybe on Langbehn's book, *"Rembrandt als Erzieher,"* for all I know. When war was declared he hung around Washington trying to get the Army to take him back. He is a veteran of the Spanish-American War. He was a sergeant with the Gatling guns at San Juan Hill. But in 1917 he was close to fifty years old and as deaf as he is now, so the Army wouldn't take him. He came back to Northern and found out what had just happened to the professor of German. He didn't know this professor of German, but he believed in academic freedom; *ordinary courtesy* is what he called it. He didn't know a lot of people in those days but, by God, he knew Nels Holgersen, and he knew what Nels had to do. So he started to raise hell around this state speaking to parent-teachers meetings, service clubs, churches, and any other group that invited him.

"Holgersen had been teaching at Northern for fifteen years, ever since he had taken his doctorate at Copenhagen in 1902. He had an amazing following of former students. Apparently every other Lutheran minister in the state had studied *Introduction to Philosophy* with him. Half the members of the legislature had also either taken a course from him or felt they should have done so in order to be politically respectable.

"The regents of Northern State University began to feel pressure from all sorts of sources. Their political associates sneered at their ineptitude. The Spanish War veterans asked them where the hell were they in 1898. Their attorneys hinted at dark legal difficulties in their possible futures. Their clergymen asked them how they could hope ever to have the Almighty look them in the face after being guilty of such a sin. Several bankers said openly that men not trusted by Professor Holgersen were obviously not good candidates for loans. It was an astounding phenomenon. It couldn't have happened anywhere with anybody, I

think, except in this state with Nels Holgersen. So the regents
had another meeting and reversed themselves."

"They took the professor of German back?" I asked.

"That was in some respects the funniest part of it," said
Handelman. "That professor had another job by this time and in
effect he said, 'The Hell with Northern State,' whereupon the
president and the regents politely asked Holgersen what to do
next. He said the professor of German should get one year's full
pay and an apology, and that, my friend, is exactly what the
regents voted to do."

"Well, I understand Langbehn's *'Rembrandt als Erzieher'*
better now," I admitted.

Handelman laughed. "Yeah," he said. "Every time we get a
chance around here we all line up as we did tonight and holler,
'Thank you, Professor Holgersen.' We understand a lot of things
better because of him."

Holgersen retired at age sixty-eight in 1936. By that time
many younger members of the faculty did not really know why
he was so popular. They thought perhaps it was just because he
was a gentleman of the old school. As I think the matter over
now, I guess that may well be the main reason we always listened
to him with great respect and shouted our thanks.

In the winter of 1938–39 the newly established School of
Education at Petaluma in the Far West began to look me over as
a possible candidate for the deanship. I visited the school and a
committee of its faculty visited me. In March, the Petaluma job
was offered to me and I accepted it.

First I went to Dean Butler and reported my decision. He
was kind in his comments and gave me a number of useful recommendations for filling vacancies in the Petaluma faculty. Then, at
Butler's insistence I went to make peace with the president.

"Petaluma will never amount to anything," snarled Handelman. "You're crazy to go there."

"What did the president of Oskaloosa say when you came
here as dean of education in 1919?" I asked.

Poplar Branch stared balefully at me while he marshaled his memory. "He told me I was crazy," he finally admitted. "He said Northern State would never amount to anything."

"Aha," I murmured triumphantly.

"The main difference between him and me," Poplar Branch added, "is that I know what I'm talking about!"

EIGHTEEN

Petaluma

WHEN I CAME to Petaluma I was forty-six years old. Until that time I had been mainly concerned with learning the various professional jobs that came my way. I was approaching a point where I might have become one of those perpetual trainees to be found in many university faculties. They are eager post-doctoral students, disciples of the more advanced theorists, leaders of various newer trends, and torch bearers for modern movements without being entirely clear as to where those movements are headed. They learn to cultivate the novel ideas of others so well that they lose their own youthful gift of original thought.

Whatever tendency I may have had in this direction was effectively blocked by coming to Petaluma. I had not been twenty-four hours on the unforgettable campus above the Pacific headlands before I knew that my days of training were over. I had moved across the frontier from professional schooling to professional experience.

This is not for a moment to imply that I learned nothing of consequence during the nineteen years I spent at Petaluma. On the contrary, I acquired new skills and formulated useful generalizations in connection with many tasks. These tasks were chiefly in administration, instruction, service, research, and communication, and certainly I gained facility in them. All this was incidental, however, to my chief role. It was subordinate to the simple circumstance that after I became dean, no one, including myself, ever again regarded me as being *in statu pupillari*.

The people at Petaluma, from the president to the youngest student, made it clear at once that they looked upon me as an authority rather than a learner. They expected me to give them evaluations, decisions, pronouncements, plans, judgments, and other bases of action. They were not concerned with my professional development. If they thought of the matter at all, they assumed that my standard of action was a finished product, perhaps at times of doubtful quality but relatively insusceptible to improvement. I was the dean, presumably by reason of previous training. Any mistakes I made were merely evidences of a lack of ability rather than a lack of educational opportunities.

Nobody cared, therefore, whether I learned anything. My colleagues and students wanted advice. If I gave them counsel that suited their wishes, they were pleased and thought I was a good dean. If I proposed action they did not like, and they happened to be friendly to me, they charged the bad advice to gaps in my education. If they were not friendly, they charged it to a perverse streak in my character. In either case they had little hope of solving the problem by educating me further. With regard to deans, moreover, they often affirmed such stereotypes of the doctrine of original administrative sin as, "You don't have to be a so-and-so to be a dean, but it helps," or, "A dean is too mean to be a professor but not mean enough to be a president."

Petaluma's president, George Hale Williams, set much of the pattern for the institution's attitude toward the new dean of the school of education. He was himself a competent administrator, but he had no interest in my administrative development. He had employed me because he believed I was able to organize and operate teacher-education programs. When we differed it was simply a case of disagreement between two experts. It was not regarded by either of us as a learning excercise.

Petaluma had been a two-year normal school until 1905. Then it was a four-year teachers college until 1937. On the latter date its name was changed to Petaluma State College and its function to that of a general four-year college which also gave masters' degrees in education and a few other subjects. At the time of this writing, of course, it is the Petaluma State University, which like others of its group has recently had a speed of growth in facilities and enrollments exceeded only by the confusion of its programs.

In the deanship of the school of education, I succeeded Walter W. Large, a professor of educational psychology, who had been at Petaluma since 1912, serving as chairman of the department of education from 1927 to 1937, and as dean of the school of education since its establishment in 1937.

Large was a good administrator. He had a very difficult set of tasks, however, and he was handicapped by long experience in subordinate jobs. He had been a professor for fifteen years before becoming a department chairman, for example, and a chairman for ten years before he became a dean. According to what may be called the *First Peddiwellian Law of Administrative Parsimony*, he had served too long on subordinate levels for optimum performance in the deanship.

This law holds that, with allowances for individual differences, a period of three to six years is enough time to spend on any administrative level in preparation for a more advanced job. The average university president, for example, who has been a dean, a director of a division, or a department chairman for longer than five or six years tends more or less unconsciously to operate or try to operate the university simply as an enlarged school, division, or department. Of course, he may be inclined to do that also as a result of merely two or three years of experience on the subordinate level, but the harsh realities of his new job in the presidency will ordinarily make him forget the details of his relatively brief experience on the previous job. If his earlier experience has been extended much beyond the crucial five-to-six-year span, however, its details have been so over-learned that responses to them lean toward the automatic. The more nearly the president's responses are automatic, the harder it is for him to make adjustments to the new all-university situation.

Some of the most bizarre educational aberrations can best be understood by looking at them in the light of this law. The precise little lady who was a third-grade teacher for eighteen years before taking an elementary principalship is likely to treat her fellow teachers as though they were third-grade pupils. The superintendent of schools who was a high-school principal for twelve years often bogs his administration down because he thinks of the whole educational system as being an extended secondary school; he was a high-school principal eight or nine years too long.

I had been an acting dean at Northern State University for one year and worked in that institution on several smaller administrative assignments, but until I came to Petaluma I had never properly appreciated the weight of a dean's job. At Petaluma I noted at once a change in my own attitude toward my role. The problems I had to solve seemed suddenly more complex than such problems appeared when I had worked on them before I became a dean. Now I was more conscious of a need to solve most of them rapidly. My attempted solutions seemed often to raise new and more difficult problems. The consciousness of my singular responsibility was forever staring over my shoulder at whatever I did.

A case involving faculty-regents relations will illustrate the general pattern of problems which the dean had to face at Petaluma. I suppose I remember this case with particular bitterness because I believed at the time, and I still believe, that my solutions were inadequate and more than faintly amateurish. Probably because of their imperfections they were generally hailed by my colleagues as examples of administrative wisdom.

The Petaluma Demonstration School, a twelve-year institution divided into elementary and secondary sections, was organized as a department of the School of Education. Its director was chairman of the department. Its teachers held academic ranks as instructors, assistant professors, and associate professors. The director, when I came to Petaluma in 1939, was a professor. In the fall of that year he was offered a city school superintendency in another state on condition that he start working at the new job on February 1, 1940. He was succeeding a superintendent who had died in office.

Since the superintendency in question was a key position in its state and since it carried a salary almost double that of a professor at Petaluma, I released the director of the Demonstration School from his obligation to complete the year at Petaluma. Then I began to search for his successor among the teachers of the Demonstration School. I soon found that none of them could be appointed director. It was not so much that they lacked capacity for the place; about a dozen of them had the requisite experience and doctoral degrees. It was rather that they were divided into three mutually suspicious, even hostile, groups, each of which urged one candidacy only. They were intense, almost fanatical, in devotion to their candidates and in the warmth of their recommendations to me.

The first group could have been called the Young Scientists' Party. Its leaders were teachers of science and mathematics. Its followers included a sprinkling of disgruntled English teachers but most of them were in the natural sciences in the secondary school. Their candidate was an amiable young man, a teacher of biology, with no administrative experience or even vague notions about administration. The second group might have been called the Humanists. It was composed of secondary teachers of history, geography, foreign languages, art, and music, and most of the elementary teachers. Their candidate was a woman, a teacher of French, who in her youth had been an elementary-school principal.

The third group was the Commercial Department. Its candidate was the head of the department, a teacher of bookkeeping and business arithmetic. He was supported by the other two members of the department, rather mature ladies who taught shorthand and typewriting. Unrequested recommendations from local business establishments and from commercial departments in other high schools also came to me in support of this candidate.

As I studied these three parties and their candidates, encouraging them all to talk freely both as individuals and in any group combinations that occurred to them, I was soon convinced that only the Humanists' candidate was even partially qualified for the directorship. She lacked the doctoral degree and the associate professorial rank which usually required that degree, but she obviously had administrative experience and capacity which the two men lacked. After discussing the situation several times she advised me (1) to act as director of the Demonstration School myself and (2) to search for a director outside the school's faculty. I offered the acting directorship to her, but she refused the appointment.

"If I took it," she said, "both those men would be humiliated."

Thereupon I followed her advice exactly. I appointed senior teachers as acting principals of the elementary and secondary sections and began to get recommendations from many sources. I carried on a heavy correspondence, visited demonstration schools on other campuses, and appointed a committee of two young Scientists, two Humanists, and the Commercial chairman to advise me at every step. Finally the committee and I agreed on three top candidates. We invited them to lecture to our student teachers, visit our school, and consult with our Demonstration faculty during three successive weeks in January and February, paying each of them his expenses and an honorarium of $100 per day. I mention all these details because a sense of guilt still haunts me when I think of this case. Was I too meticulous? Was I not careful enough?

I asked each member of the Demonstration School faculty to advise me, either orally or in writing, concerning these three candidates. They were generally, though not unanimously, in agreement that a man whom I will call Norman Nelson because that was not his name, was the superior candidate. They recommended that I offer him the directorship with the beginning rank of associate professor and a salary appropriate to the rank. After clearing this recommendation with President Williams, I wrote to Nelson and made him the offer. He accepted.

In my letter to Nelson, I stated, as was customary, that if his answer was favorable, I would recommend him to the president who would then recommend his appointment to the board of regents at their next meeting. This, I said was our system, and it usually operated smoothly after the dean's recommendation, but the final appointment was made by the regents.

The board met early in March, and Nelson's name was in a list of about twenty nominees from the School of Education. Most of them were instructors and assistant professors on first appointments. There were three nominations to professor and four to associate professor; all of them except Nelson were for promotions within our own ranks.

The morning after the regents' meeting, the president called me to his office.

"All recommendations for appointments in the School of Education," he began, "were approved by the regents . . ." whereupon I said, "Good," and then wondered at the president's seeming embarrassment. "Except," he continued, "that of Nelson."

"Excuse me. I didn't mean to interrupt," I said. "Why did they refuse to appoint him?"

"They didn't refuse," explained the president. "They just deferred action on that appointment and asked me to request you —er—unofficially to investigate Nelson's qualifications a little further."

Ten years earlier I would have been flaring into anger at this point, but now I kept at least outwardly calm and listened to the president's account of the board meeting.

One of the regents, a prominent lawyer from the capital of the state, named Harley, had told the board that he had some confidential information which indicated subversive tendencies in Nelson's past. He had made the request that the dean investigate the candidate further and make an additional report to the regents.

"What was the source of Mr. Harley's information?" I asked.

"A friend of his in the city back East where Nelson is now employed told him in strictest confidence that this man should not be employed by Petaluma," explained President Williams.

"And the detailed charges were what?" I inquired.

"Well, that Nelson has a bad reputation for radicalism," said the president.

I had already made my decision to comply fully with the request. I left the president's office with a plan of action in mind. My first task was the most unpleasant one, so I had to get it over with rapidly. I wired Nelson: FINAL APPOINTMENT DELAYED UNTIL APRIL MEETING OF BOARD. HOPE YOU WILL NOT BE UNDULY INCONVENIENCED. Then I began to check air and train schedules. I went first to the city where Nelson was principal of a university high school. I interviewed the dean of the school of education under whose supervision the high school operated, five members of the high-school faculty, the president of the parent-teachers association of that school, and the commander of the local post of a veterans' organization to which Nelson belonged. I told each of them that my university was considering the appointment of Nelson to a position of considerable importance. I said I was especially interested in their judgments of his personal qualities, his reputation in the community, how he got along with his associates, and his general trustworthiness. I did not ask anyone a specific question about his patriotism. Nelson knew I was making this additional inquiry, of course. I called on him as soon as I entered his city and told him that I was getting these additional recommendations. An inquiry about patriotism would have suggested at once that someone had questioned it. I therefore deliberately left it out of the interviews.

All the respondents gave Nelson good recommendations, some of them glowing with friendship for him. After each interview, in private, I made carefully detailed notes of all responses.

Next I went to a smaller city where Nelson had been an elementary-school principal and made a similar investigation with similar results.

Finally I traveled to the university where Nelson had taken his doctorate. There I interviewed the vice-president in charge of academic affairs, the dean of the graduate school, the four living members of his doctoral committee, and three men on the staff of the school of education who had been his fellow graduate students. One of the latter, in general conversation, said, "This university was a lively place in those days. We had two boys from our graduate club in the Spanish Civil War. It's a wonder more of us didn't go."

"Was Nelson especially concerned about that war?" I asked.

"I don't believe he was," said my informant. "His chief concern was to finish his dissertation, as I remember it."

I put all this in my notes and returned to Petaluma. There I wrote a summary of my findings, repeated my recommendation that Nelson be appointed associate professor, and gave the document to the president. The next day he called me by telephone and asked me to have a personal interview with Regent Harley.

"Why?" I asked.

"Well, you know," said the president. "He is worried about this Nelson matter, and if we can soothe him down, the next board meeting will run more smoothly."

Again I stifled my resentment and agreed to confer with Mr. Harley in the presence of Dr. Williams. The president said he was leaving almost immediately to attend a convention in Washington, D.C., and would not return until just before the next board meeting. He asked me as a special favor to confer alone with Harley and "soothe him down." I said that I would do the best I could.

Harley was a birdlike man, even to having a chirping manner of speech. He beamed at me and said he was looking forward to my report on Nelson. "You have it with you, of course?" he said.

"No," I replied. "I gave it to the president. He will present it to the board."

"But you have a copy with you?" chirped Harley.

"No," I said, "and if I did have one, it would be entirely improper of me to give it to one member of the board before it is presented to the other members in a regular meeting."

"Oh," said Harley, as though someone had stolen his birdseed. He seemed cast down. He gave the impression that he felt he had missed out on a great experience. At this point I began to develop the thesis that this man was basically a gossip, that he loved the practice of law for the opportunities it offered for the acquisition of confidential dirt on his fellow citizens. He wanted first chance at derogatory information on Nelson so that he could pass it on to other regents before the board meeting.

"You found evidence of what my friend reported on Nelson?" he asked.

"None whatever," I replied.

"You must have overlooked something," he said accusingly.

"Why don't you tell me who your friend is and exactly what he reported concerning Nelson?" I inquired.

"Oh, no," he cried. "I couldn't do that!"

"Why not?" I persisted.

"It would be a betrayal of my friend's confidence," he said.

I could feel my temper beginning to slip, but I think I did not show it. I merely remarked, as I rose to leave, "You are worried about your friend's confidence. Have you considered Nelson's reputation?"

Harley looked blank at this and protested that we needed to study this case further.

"Did you inquire about any sex irregularities?" he asked.

"I did not," I said. "You will see what I asked when you read the report. I have nothing further to add except that I have been away from my office for more than a week and I have extra work to do."

I report this conversation since I understand that Harley claimed I was impolite to him. I did not then and I do not now see anything in my manner or speech that was discourteous. In view of the steadily growing contempt I had for this bird, I still believe that I was a paragon of politeness in my dealings with him. I suspect that he thought any faculty member was impolite to him who did not at least metaphorically kiss his hands.

I was called into the next board meeting. When the president announced that we would turn to the unfinished business of the

Nelson appointment, saying that everyone had seen a copy of my report, Harley chirped brightly, without properly addressing the president first, "Of course, we don't want to worry you, Dean Peddiwell, but . . . ."

"You don't worry me," I interposed, and now I knew that my training days were over and that I was merely repeating a lesson long since learned. "I am not worried, Mr. Harley. People worry when they do not know what to do in a particular situation. I know very clearly what to do if my recommendation concerning this appointment is rejected. You will have my resignation on that table, and the newspapers of this state will have a full explanation of why I resigned."

"Are you threatening the board?" called Harley.

"Threatening? Certainly not. I am just explaining to you why I am not worried. Is there any member of the board, other than Mr. Harley who has already examined me in private, who has an additional question on this case? If not, and if you do not need me further, Mr. President, may I be excused?"

President Williams looked sad as he gave me permission to leave. I remember a fleeting wave of pity for him, but then I thought, *Presidents are not supposed to be happy. Like deans, professors, and students, they are supposed to be significant.*

Nelson's appointment was approved, with Harley dissenting.

Nelson did a competent job in the directorship for six years, the last two of them with the rank of professor. Then he took a deanship at an Eastern university where he often spoke favorably of his Petaluma experience. Sometimes he added, I am told, "Dean Peddiwell was very genial and easygoing but he was afraid of the president and the regents. He made me wait an extra month for my original appointment because he was too timid to lay down the law to the administration."

I will report another illustration of how my professional education ended as the stark realities of professional experience took over in the events of my deanship.

It was in the winter of 1953. The legislature was in session. President Williams was in a hospital for minor surgery. As senior dean I went with the comptroller to represent the university at a budget hearing before the House committee on education. One of the other state colleges was represented by its newly appointed president, a modest-appearing young man who was well but somewhat conservatively dressed. Under his perfectly tailored coat, he wore a vest across which extended a slender gold chain bearing a Phi Beta Kappa key. I looked at him admiringly. He was a clear example of what a successful college administrator should look like.

At first I was not listening closely as the president was being questioned by the chairman. I was merely hearing the usual political patter designed to convince the public that the legislature was making heroic efforts to reduce the tax burdens which were grinding down the faces of the poor. Then suddenly, to my astonishment, the questioning was taken over by another member of the committee who seemed to be heckling the president on personal matters.

The heckler was a big red-faced man whom I did not know. I assumed that he was a new member of the legislature, although he spoke with the easy authority of an old-timer.

"What did you do for a living before you got this job?" he asked.

"I was a professor and later a dean at one of the state universities in the Middle West," replied the president, naming the institution.

"Professor of what?" demanded the committee member.

"Of sociology," said the president.

"Sociology? What's that?"

"It's the study of society, of social groups." The president was obviously trying to make his answer accurate, yet simple enough for the questioner's understanding.

"Society? The Four Hundred, huh?"

"Well, no. Sociology deals rather with ..." began the president, but his inquisitor interrupted.

"And you said you were a dean. Dean of what?"

"The College of Arts, Letters, and Sciences."

I looked at the committee chairman, wondering how long he would permit this clearly inappropriate line of questioning. Apparently the red-faced man fancied himself a lawyer, whether or not he had the diploma. The chairman sat with a vacuous half-smile on his face, however, as though he had little interest in the proceedings. I was disturbed by his remissness. Twelve years earlier he had been an undergraduate in one of my classes. He had taught only one year and had then gone to war, after which he had entered politics. I was about ready to fail him *ex post facto* for allowing this studied persecution of the young president to continue.

"What's that thing hangin' on your watch-chain?" demanded the red-faced questioner.

"Why—uh—it's a Phi Beta Kappa key," said the president, showing signs of embarrassment for the first time.

"Phi Beta Kappa? What's that?"

"It's a scholarship society."

"Shows you're pretty smart, huh?" The heckler was now sneering openly. Another member of the committee objected that everybody's time was being wasted, and at last the chairman came out of his trance and began to direct the questioning along budgetary lines.

The next institution to have its budget discussed was Petaluma. As I stood up to present our case, I was glad to see the young president leaving the committee room. I did not want him to be further embarrassed by hearing what I was planning to say.

The chairman greeted me warmly. "We hope that President Williams will soon be out of the hospital," he said, "but we are always glad to see you, Dean."

"Thank you, Mr. Chairman," I said. "With your kind permission I should like to preface my part in this hearing with a personal statement."

The chairman's smile faded. "Personal statement?" he repeated. "Why—er—yes, sir, go ahead."

"I thought it would be all right," I said, "since there was a lot of personal discussion here a little while ago. I assume it is the way to begin." The chairman looked grave but said nothing. "I am a school teacher," I continued, "working for my bosses. I started teaching forty-two years ago and except for military service and university attendance I have been a teacher, principal, superintendent of schools, professor of education, or dean of education ever since. When I went to the university I had the honor to be elected to the Society of Phi Beta Kappa. I have never known anyone who ever attended a college or university who did not know what Phi Beta Kappa was and did not regard membership in it as an honorable status. I have never known a parent of a university student who was so stupid as to be ashamed to have a son or daughter elected to Phi Beta Kappa."

"Look, Dean," broke in the red-faced member. "I was just joking. I wasn't talking about you."

"And I am not talking to you," I said. "I am speaking to the chairman of this committee on personal matters. As a school teacher I always try to work faithfully for my bosses, and I know who they are. At present they are the people of this state as represented by the regents of my university. If the regents decide they no longer need my services, they have only to tell me and I will try to get a job elsewhere. If I don't like the regents' decision on any matter, I can resign and appeal directly to my bosses, the people. They are the bosses of the legislature too, I understand. Am I correct in this assumption?"

"You are absolutely right, Dean," said the chairman.

"Thank you, sir," I said. "I'll be glad now to try to answer questions that you or any member of the committee may wish to direct to me."

The questions were simple, and none of them came from the red-faced man.

No one has ever asked me what I would have done if the red-faced member had tried to heckle me. I know what I would have done. I would have done my best to destroy him politically. I do not think it would have been a very difficult task. As a matter of final record, he was defeated in the next election by an alumnus of Petaluma and he never held another elective office.

In this case as in the Nelson incident and others that I might recount, I was simply repeating lessons I had learned earlier, applying them to the Petaluma problems. I was always awkward and sometimes too severe in their application. I was in practice and not in training. I wish I could say that I did the best I could, but I am afraid that would not be completely accurate.

NINETEEN

Hoka Hey!

IN THE OLD LACOTAH DAYS the warriors painted themselves and their horses in colors appropriate to the coming mission, mounted with lance or carbine at the ready, and then rode out shouting, *"Hoka hey!"*

The expression was not exactly one of farewell, although it might sometimes be so interpreted. It carried no promise of return, no hint of *au revoir* or *so long*. It was not primarily a war cry, although it could be one when the battle was joined. It was more an invitation to arms. Its direct meaning was, "Move out! Let's go!" Its indirect meanings were carried by powerful overtones which signaled, "Now is the time! There are *coups* to be struck for our people! This is a good day to die!"

Because this story has tried to recount some of the educational *coups* in my life, both those I struck and those I missed, I write this final chapter as a *hoka hey* call. I write it not as a bear soldier, old and wise, nor even as a mature member of the kit fox lodge, astute and wily, but as a simple-minded dog warrior who would ride once more for our people.

I am not very wise. I am not very astute. But I see the mission. Now, therefore, let us look carefully and critically at it. Let us make sure that we recognize it and understand it. Then it is up to us to rope our horses, paint them in the right colors, pick up our weapons, mount, and ride.

The education of an individual has to serve a mission or it ceases to be education. Education improves the learner's capacity to carry out his mission, builds up the skills he needs for the mission, and moves him into the action the mission demands. The educational processes must move the man or the group forward toward clearly seen goals. Whenever those processes begin to deteriorate the capacities and regress the person or the society away from the mission, they no longer constitute education but merge into a reverse phenomenon.

No language of which I have any knowledge possesses a word for this reverse of education. The reason for such a linguistic gap is evident. No society has enough insight and courage to face the stark possibility that its would-be educational efforts are cutting its cultural throat. Almost always in this situation the society's wise old men begin to fuss with facts, classify curricula, and throw verbal sand over their left shoulders rather than approach the tough and often dangerous job of studying and criticizing their mission.

For the purpose of this discussion, I beg the reader to let me suggest a word here to fill this gap. I propose the term, *detriation*. Education is experience that improves, builds up, and moves a person or a group forward; detriation is experience that wears down, deteriorates, and regresses the individual or the society. Whether an experience is educational or detriational depends, therefore, upon where the learner or the learning group is headed. What is the mission, the goal, the dream of this man or this society? If the experience serves the dream, it is education; if it thwarts the dream, it is detriation.

For my first notions of this principle, I must credit J. J. Webster's story of how Tom Gunn's mule swam the Columbia River three times and then collapsed from thirst.

This animal had excellent native endowment. He weighed 1100 pounds and stood sixteen hands high. His father was a registered Andalusian jack; his mother was half German coach horse and half Eastern Oregon bronco. Through some detriational quirk in his early experience, however, he was peculiarly liable to

onfusion of his goals; hence the common expression in Umatilla
County, Oregon, "No more sense than Tom Gunn's mule."

One summer when ranch work was slack, this mule was graz-
ing with other range animals in the Horse Heaven country of
Washington, just across the Columbia River from Umatilla. On a
hot July day it occurred to him that he was thirsty. He had not
been to water that day or even the day before. So he started at a
steady trot for the Columbia River about five miles away.

If you had asked this mule what his purpose was, no doubt
he would have replied, "To get a drink." Actually he had another
and more dominant purpose that often overrode his attention to
immediate goals. This purpose was to keep other creatures from
ridiculing his ears. He was abnormally sensitive about his ears.

On this day he came plunging down the bank toward a little
sandy beach where he had often drunk before, his eyes fixed on
the water, his nostrils dilating in anticipation. Just as he moved
through the last clumps of sagebrush, however, a startled jackrabbit sat up and stared at him, moving its ears in alternate fore
and aft stances. The mule forgot his thirst in a quick flash of
anger.

"What are you lookin' at?" he snarled.

The rabbit, conscious only of a snorting, lathered mule who
seemed to be hostile, dropped its ears back over its shoulders and
took off. The mule, seeing primarily those ears, every movement
of which seemed to be insulting, charged after the rabbit, his
front hooves flying for the kill. "I'll learn you not to make fun of
me," he yelled.

The rabbit ducked, dodged, circled, and finally hid in a clump
of sage just short of the water's edge. The mule plunged into the
stream, swimming strongly toward Oregon, raising his head occasionally in an attempt to sight his tormentor who, he thought,
was swimming ahead of him. When he reached the opposite shore
he flushed an Oregon jackrabbit who looked like the Washington
one and moved its ears in the same insulting fashion. Why did
not the mule note at once that this new rabbit's fur was dry and
that it could not have just emerged from the river? Ah! This is a

crucial question, and its answer is equally crucial. The mule could not, would not, look at any evidence that clashed with his view of his mission. His detriation on ear-sensitivity had taken care of that.

The mule followed this rabbit's evasive flight, lost it at the water's edge, and swam back to Washington trying to overtake it. The poor animal was very tired now, but when the original rabbit or its twin jumped from the sage, waggled its ears, and began its circling, he started bravely after it, snorting vengeance, lost it at the water's edge, and swam the river again, this third time quite slowly for even his great strength was ebbing fast. At last he staggered up on the Oregon bank, trying to locate that rabbit. At the high-water line he tripped over a piece of driftwood and fell heavily. There he lay, too exhausted to rise, and there he might have died of thirst if Tom Gunn himself had not come to his aid. The rancher, riding along the river road, had seen the animal stagger out of the water and fall. "That looks like my crazy dun mule," he said, and as he rode closer he saw that sure enough it was. He brought a hatful of water to revive the animal and then noted that the mule was very thirsty. He brought another hatful of water and let the mule drink. Next he put a rope around the patient's neck, snubbed the rope to his saddle horn, and pulled the mule to his feet.

"Talk about a feller that don't know enough to come in outa the rain," mused Tom Gunn. "Here is a Goddamn mule so dumb he can swim the Columbia River and not know enough to take a drink!"

Is it possible to discover the breakdown in this mule's education by looking first at the "subjects" he had studied, the items of knowledge he had acquired, and the skills he had developed? He knew local geography, for example, and he knew much of it more intimately than did Tom Gunn himself. There were few trails in Horse Heaven and on the whole Gunn Ranch with which that mule was not familiar. He knew the river flowed between Horse Heaven and his home range? He had swum that river so often that the distance across it was stamped into his muscles and central nervous system. He knew where the best patches of bunch grass grew; his memory of them had been re-enforced by hunger. He had many skills also. He had been broken to harness, and he knew how to put his weight into a collar. He knew how to defend himself too, as a yapping dog one day sadly discovered. When the dog nipped at the mule's heels and then ducked down to avoid the swinging kick customarily employed by horses, the mule did not swing his hind foot in an arc. He looked back and aimed a well-calked shoe straight into the dog's face.

All such items of knowledge and skill were merely instruments for the mule. Whether they were educational or detriational instruments cannot be determined just by examining them alone. They had educational or detriational meaning only in terms of the mule's mission and the motives that drove him out on that mission.

Consider a framework against which my autobiography or the personal history of anyone may be checked to judge its educational meaning and quality. Tom Gunn's mule showed that this judgment cannot be made simply by looking at the disciplines studied. The important items to scrutinize in the life of J. Abner Peddiwell are not whether he learned in the reservation school to extract cube roots or memorize the boundaries and capitals of the then forty-five states, whether he studied Greek or manual training in the Tum-a-Lum Academy, whether he pursued the calculus or art appreciation in the University of the West, or whether his doctoral dissertation dealt with the field guns at Brice's Crossroads or the love life of the common barnacle. All such matters were interesting, often useful, but never more than subsidiary.

Subsidiary to what?

They were subsidiary to answers to the following groups of questions about the schooling and its resultant education or detriation of any man:

1. What was the man's dominant mission? What dream lay behind his efforts to acquire an education? From what corners and angles of his background and particularly from what

people did his dream arise? Into what features of his character and personality did the dream extend?

2. What motivated the man to pursue his mission? What was
his drive to learning? From what sources did it come? To
what extent did it serve the mission? Did it sometimes even
block the accomplishment of the mission? How did it affect
the course of the man's schooling?

3. What was the man's learning style? Where did he acquire
it? How was it exemplified in his choice of subjects? In his
methods of study? In his own techniques as a teacher?

4. What were the chief outcomes of the man's schooling? To
what extent were they educational or detriational? What kind
of person did he become? How far did he drift from his
mission?

As I try to answer these questions with regard to my own
educational life and times, I can say that my concept of a personal mission was primarily one of serving my people by helping
them change their ways through schooling. Those boyhood day-
dreams which I best remember always had me in some teaching
role. I do not now recall ever yearning to be an important soldier,
for instance. I do not believe that I ever wanted to command men,
although I had that experience early thrust upon me, sometimes
in a spectacular manner. I wanted instead to communicate with
them, to understand them, and to have them understand me. I
wanted to teach them and have them teach me.

Now that I examine my military memories, it occurs to me
that the small successes I had in military-command situations
were probably the results of teaching rather than of commanding
skills.

What has been said here about my small interest in military
achievement might be repeated with even greater emphasis with
respect to any dream of becoming wealthy. I had no interest
whatsoever in thinking what I would do with large sums of
money. No doubt much of this lack of interest in wealth arose in
part from never needing money very badly. It is true that as a boy

I worked for laborers' wages, but the fact remained that I was J. J. Webster's son and was thereby not fully immersed in the economic struggle.

I believe that I acquired the concept of my mission from all my teachers. Perhaps it is more accurate to say that anyone who gave me an element of my dream was by virtue of that fact my teacher. When J. J. Webster testified, "I would sure like to have been a teacher if I had ever acquired even the minimum of necessary schooling," when Medicine Horse said, "I tell you these old stories because I want you to be good men, good for our people," and when William Preston MacFarland asked, "Is this perhaps a case where human rights take precedence over property rights?" each of them was shaping young Abner Peddiwell's dream of his mission. The Living Word of the Danebod community also affected the boy's dream, and in that respect Bishop Nicolai F. S. Grundtvig was one of his teachers.

It is very difficult, of course, to say just where the making of a man's dream begins or ends, but certainly the main elements of Peddiwell's concept of his mission were profoundly reinforced by the administrative pattern of Poplar Branch Handelman and the action-expressed views of Henry Liberty Brown, Matt Higby, Willem Van Ek, Robert E. L. Woods, James Clark, Nels Holgersen, and a multitude of others, some of them whose names Peddiwell never knew. Indeed there were many of his very important teachers, like Bishop Grundtvig, whom he never saw. There were others whom he never saw in life but was proud to ride past their bodies, fighting in the same quarrel in which they had died.

I must have acquired the first elements of the dream very early, probably when I was still a young child. I do not remember ever having difficulty in recognizing any man who operated under the aegis of that dream. This may have been a delusion; if so, it was a useful and comforting one. It gave direction and substance to my schooling. It gave me confidence in my ability to distinguish between education and detriation in my own case and in the case of my own people.

The dream, the concept of the mission, in a man's schooling

often seems to dominate or even determine the drive to learning, the basic motivation. Observation of many cases over many years, however, inclines me to suspect that this is always an illusion. The drive serves the dream so closely in a well-coordinated individual that the two factors appear to merge, but this is only an appearance. They are always separate; they can come from very different sources; one can be present in strength and the other almost completely lacking. The drive can sometimes block the dream, and the dream often negates the drive. Let me illustrate some of these developments from the experience of Peddiwell.

When Abner was very young he received most of his drive from the personalities close to him. When he got Rain-in-the-Face for a birthday present, he did not need to be urged to groom the beautiful black horse carefully every day. Ever since he could remember he had had at least a burro to groom and other pet animals to care for. He saw the ranch-hands going about their duties without outward prompting. Anyone who needed to be harangued into doing his work did not last long on the Bar-W. Indeed he was not likely ever to be employed there. Both J. J. Webster and Levi Kingman were practical psychologists who could spot a drive at a glance.

The boy grew up with the examples of Mr. Webster and Levi constantly before him. Here were men who obviously were under no outward compulsion to action. They were driven to unremitting labor, hardships, even pain by something within themselves. Young Abner assumed, no doubt, that he too had an inner drive, that all men had it to some degree, and that its quality and power were vital elements in a man's character and personality.

Certainly after September, 1899, Abner had a name for his own drive. He got it when he raised the new carbine in the gift gesture to Medicine Horse, as Mr. Webster had instructed him to do, looked straight into the slender chief's eyes, and then thought triumphantly as the old Indian smiled, *He saw* wakan *in my eyes*.

In the many years that have passed since that September day outside Medicine Horse's teepee, the *wakan* has never left me. While a man's mission can and should be comprehended in a rational manner, and while it can and should be refined and sometimes changed by the acquisition of new information, his drive is a *wakan* thing that is not built up by slow accretions. It comes to him in a flash of insight. Once he has it, he will not relinquish it or modify it easily. When the bugle sounds *Fix Bayonets,* the *wakan* grips Private Peddiwell and he moves automatically. From the outside he may appear to be a cold automaton but inside a warm consciousness floods his whole being, *When this regiment has its bayonets fixed it cannot be whipped.* When the university professor sketches possible investigations for his seminar members, Graduate Student Peddiwell is unaware of ordinary campus motivation; he is listening only to the *wakan* that taps him on the shoulder and demands the fullest possible measure of originality and labor. Other students may be thinking of marks, perhaps even saying that *C* is a gentleman's grade, but the motivations they experience are pallid wraiths beside Peddiwell's drive. Marks do not fit his *wakan*. When Superintendent, Professor, or Dean Peddiwell responds most swiftly and confidently to an unfriendly move against his institutions or his people, it is usually not because his mission is menaced but rather because his *wakan* is threatened.

When we turn to the third question, that of the man's educational style, we note that drive and style are very closely related but are clearly separate factors. A man's drive to learning is the father of his style. If the drive is strong and persistent, it requires and tends to develop a clearcut and powerful style. If it is weak and uncertain, it begets a sloppy and stumbling style. The basis for this connection between drive and style is evident. The *wakan* has to go from man to man among the learners. The Living Word has to be passed from generation to generation in unmistakable form. The humane purposes have to be unforgettably known. The administrative patterns have to be clearly understood or they will not work.

The style of my own learning and teaching was definitely tied to my peculiar drive. Its heart was a desire for clear and memorable exposition. This is why, when I am asked to define education, I think of it first as a special and powerful instrument of communication.

My style came from the same sources as those which had given me the drive. It came from all my teachers, not only the famous and highly skilled ones but also even the most obscure and uncertain members of the craft. This explains why I cannot now recall ever having had a teacher whose instruction wearied me. I was always interested in analyzing his style if in nothing else. I studied his methods, his materials, his apparent objectives, and the ways in which he sought to reach them. I think I was not so much looking for models as for stimuli to development of my own style.

Mr. Webster's solemn tales of coyotes, mules, and jackrabbits; Medicine Horse's, "Now I was not afraid—I had something to do for my people"; Bill Reigner's, "Somebody *had* to be your second—you didn't know anybody"; Matt Higby's social dexterity in, "I'll lend you these gloves to pertect your lily-white hands"; Van Ek's. "Every man is entitled to miss the drill once in a while"; Sergeant Cobb's unswerving devotion to truth even when a vision of the chilling words, "...death or such other punishment as a court martial may direct..." was staring him in the face; Nels Holgersen's willingness not only to accept a simple principle of justice but also to do battle for it; and Poplar Branch Handelman's ready forgetting of all bruises as soon as the fight was over: these and a thousand other teachings from my masters all seemed to be woven into one opulent tapestry against whose background I was forever fated to parade my own instructional wares.

The result might well have been predicted early in my professional career. I was never satisfied with my style. It was not rich enough; it was not sharp enough; it was not swift enough, it was not precise enough; it was simply not good enough. I was always tinkering with it, always trying out new theories of how to improve it, always seeking new ways to understand it and make it work better. I was especially critical of it when my associates were most complimentary about my ideas or activities. As I grew

older I moved steadily toward the ultimate arrogance of believing
that the only proper final judge of Peddiwell's style was Peddiwell
himself. As a matter of professional accuracy, this position is not
so arrogant as it is realistic. Every learner is his own most important teacher, and if he does not know how to examine critically
his methods and theories, he is quite unlikely to have the ability
to profit from outside criticism.

My style also affected materially my choices of subjects for
study. My interest in linguistics, in mathematics as a special language, and in history, anthropology, and sociology was undoubtedly dictated by an overall conviction that a teacher must know
how to talk to his people, must seek continually to understand
their motivations and values, and must observe them closely in
action at every opportunity. I could do no less if I were to help
them change their ways in the direction of their ideals.

As we come now to the fourth set of questions concerning a
man's schooling, I am aghast that I even attempt to answer such
inquiries about myself. But the code under which an autobiographer must operate is severe at this point. It says to me; *Mister,
you have told about your mission, what you were trying to do.
You have spoken of the* wakan *that drove you into action to
achieve that dream. You have described the main features of the
style of learning and teaching by which you sought to implement
your drive to the dream. Now tell us of the outcomes of your
schooling. When were they educational and when detriational?
What kind of person did they help produce? Did you deviate a
great deal from your misson? What caused the deviation? A failure in your drive? The defects of your style? Or merely the result
of original sin antedating all your schooling?*

As I try to answer some of these questions, I am aware that
the perceptive reader can probably answer most of them more
accurately than I. What I have to say here, therefore, may be regarded as data which the reader may employ or ignore at his dis-
cretion in judging the outcomes of my schooling.

Throughout my life, the single factor which I feared most
was a tendency toward violence. Sometimes it was physical vio-

lence, of course, but more often it was psychological. It ran like
an alien thread through the pattern of my mission, it served too
often as a chief expression of my drive, and in many cases it dis-
figured my style of action.

It would be too simple to blame extended military service at
an impressionable age for much of this tendency. I had it long before I ever took the soldier's oath. I grew up among men who were
usually kind but could become dangerous in a moment over what
they regarded as matters of personal *wakan*. They rode into
Western valleys while hostile Indian smoke signals were still rising from the surrounding hills. Although they founded churches
almost as soon as the endgates had been dropped on their wagon
boxes, they were not generally other-cheek-turners or devotees of
a-soft-answer-turneth-away-wrath doctrines. They rode their
horses straight up with a carbine under the left stirrup leather,
and they commonly wore handguns not merely as weapons but
also as symbols of their conviction that one man was as good as
another and sometimes a damned sight better.

At the same time many of these men were highly disciplined
persons who could and often did exercise phenomenal self-control.
A considerable number of those who were middle-aged and older
during my youth, like Mr. Webster himself, had marched and
fought in the world's most thoroughly disciplined professional
military outfit of its time, the Army of the Potomac. They were
wary of violence, but when they judged it had to be done they
moved directly and fast into its full employment.

By the time I had entered Dr. Brown's academy, I was
steeped in this double-barreled notion of alternating self-control
with occasional violence. My experience with the civilized children and parents of the Danebod community helped me a great
deal in strengthening the self-control phase of my emotional herit-
age. Later experiences at the University of the West, culminating
in my expulsion from that institution, showed that I might have
profited greatly by longer service at Danebod. Some of my military ineptitude underscored my deficiency as did also the un-

fortunate attack five years later on the Ku Klux Klan emissary in River Junction.

Even after I became dean at Petaluma, my clash with Regent Harley over Norman Nelson's appointment and my unnecessarily severe handling of the legislator, who was guilty only of a breach of ordinary manners, indicated either that my schooling had been inadequate or that I was relatively impervious to instruction on emotional matters.

I hesitate to mention one more item in this connection, but it is possible that I suffered some detriational effect from knowing at an early age that my father had died with frontier honor in a blaze of violence. Even today in places where physical conflict might develop, I often carry a substantial clasp knife that could be used as a weapon. Sometimes as I oil my father's boot knife, I find myself tossing it a bit to weigh its balance. I have had it on my person in every military action in which I have engaged, and if the drums of war roll again for my country and she can use me again in battle I will carry that boot knife again. If this be the result of a life-long detriation, let any who will, make the most of it. I am *Abner* Peddiwell first, *J*. Abner Peddiwell second, and J. Abner Peddiwell, *Ph. D.* a long last.

Having confessed a chief weakness in the results of my schooling, I look now for some countervailing strength. The chief one, perhaps the only one of importance that I can cite, is my relative insusceptibility to an administrative defect dramatized in Lord Acton's famous dictum, *All power corrupts and absolute power corrupts absolutely*. I do not believe that power ever corrupted me very much, and I am certain that it was my schooling that protected me against that particular form of detriation. At the outset, the mission as my teachers gave it to me blocked any such development. A pupil of J. J. Webster, William Preston Mac-Farland, and Poplar Branch Handelman would be the first to sneer at himself and bring himself up on a short rein whenever he noted the slightest sign that he was beginning to exercise power for its own sweet little sake.

But, you might object at this point, *suppose the dean or other two-bit power-holder does not, perhaps cannot, recognize the signs of impending detriation in his increasing authority?*

Ah! Here is where his drive and style take over. If he was ever a pupil of Medicine Horse, he will warn himself, *This is for your people, not for you. It does not fit your* wakan *to inflate your authority. The greatest thing you can do is not to extend your power but to pick out the best day and the best cause in which to die. Listen to your* wakan *and it will tell you these things. You may not have to die now, but you must select your terrain, place your guns, form your battalions, and move out for your people, as though this were your last engagement.*

I am afraid all this sounds like an over-counting of *coups,* and I will now desist.

Our people today, as always, are in desperate need of proper education. They have glimpses of the mission, here and there, all over the world. They have elaborate and complex styles of schooling in various favored parts of the earth and at least token schooling in almost all areas of the world. The people's schooling often slips into detriation, however, because they are not altogether sure of their mission. Even more devastating in its detriational effects is their lack of a dominant drive, a spirit, a *wakan.*

The greatest task before us, the teachers of the world, is to give our people this drive. We know the mission. We must be cultivators and bearers of the driving spirit to carry out the mission. If our style is not equal to the task, let us re-make the style. We know how to do that too.

I have tried to pass this *wakan* to our teachers and to all our people. I ride out now, calling, *Hoka hey!*

> Once, when a century and I were young,
>   I told time by the bugle, at gray dawn
> It warned of zero, when the battle hung
>   In doubt, "Fix bayonets!" it sang, "Begone
> "With that barrage and do not halt for rest
>   "Or pain until above the screaming shell

"You hear me sound recall;" I did my best,
  Not much, but thus it took me straight to hell
  And back, that bugle. Now we mark time by bell,
    By schedule, by the little tricks and tools
  Of day and year; the hour we cannot tell,
    Without a bugle we are time-less fools!
Yet here's field music; can we not learn to sound
A call of spirit men will rally 'round?

ABOUT THE AUTHOR

Although many school men and women acknowledge acquaintance with J. Abner Peddiwell, Ph.D., it is generally admitted that only Harold R. W. Benjamin, emeritus professor of education at the George Peabody College for Teachers and former dean of the College of Education at the University of Maryland, has ever worked closely with the Petaluma eccentric. "He is a kinsman of mine," Benjamin said recently, "but we have somewhat different backgrounds. It is true that we came from the same Western country, served in the Army together, and were schooled in rather similar institutions. I wish to state emphatically, however, that I never attended the University of the West and I was not actually a mule-skinner in the Punitive Expedition of 1916 into Mexico. Furthermore, I am a student of comparative education, a field in which Peddiwell makes no claims to competence. I think he has never been overseas except under arms."